Emotional Health

Emotional Health

Emotional Health

what emotions are &

how they cause social & mental diseases.

Dr Bob Johnson

Consultant Psychiatrist   GMC speciality register for psychiatry

formerly   Head of Therapy, Ashworth Maximum Security Hospital, Liverpool
Consultant Psychiatrist, Special Unit, C-Wing, Parkhurst Prison, Isle of Wight .

*MRCPsych (Member of Royal College of Psychiatrists),
MRCGP (Member of Royal College of General Practitioners).
Diploma in Neurology & Psychiatry (Psychiatric Inst NY),
MA (Psychol), PhD(med computing), MBCS, DPM, MRCS.*

First published in paperback in Great Britain in 2002 by James Nayler Foundation, P O Box 235, York, YO1 7YW, UK.
www.TruthTrustConsent.com

Dr Bob Johnson is hereby identified as the author of this work in accordance with Section 77 of the Copyright, Designs and Patents Act 1988.

British Library Cataloguing in Publication Data. A CIP record of this book is available on request from the British Library.   ISBN 1-904327-00-1

Reprinted March 2003
10 9 8 7 6 5 4 3 2 -

If you have comments please send them either via the publisher or www.TruthTrustConsent.com.   Sadly, time and age will limit my replies.

<u>Please note</u> – the emotions described in this book are the real thing – and they can be deadly.   However, nothing written here excuses, nor remotely justifies any atrocity – but if we don't look at the reasons why they occur, we can never prevent them happening again, and again, and again, and again, and again.   If we do, we can.

The book was written in early 2000 – but it goes to the roots of terrorism, by describing the cause and cure of terror.

The James Nayler Foundation – Admin office P O Box 235 York YO1 7YW UK –
Incorporated in England & Wales Company Reg. number 3383970 –
Registered Charity number 1072133.   **email** – admin@TruthTrustConsent.com
www.TruthTrustConsent.com

foreword

Emotions are the single most vital ingredient in all human affairs. Yet neither my medical school nor my Cambridge University psychology degree taught me anything useful about them. The tabloid media runs riot with them, politics and commerce stir them whenever they can – it's called marketing – but too many psychiatrists, psychologists and scientists remain convinced that emotions are defunct. Not a single human transaction, from falling in love to nuclear war, can possibly occur without them – yet our academic institutions insist on treating emotions as anathema.

Emotions have been banished to the periphery for too long – time to put them back at the very heart of our human lives where they belong. Human relations come in a wide range – intimate, institutional, industrial, international – each one has at its heart an emotional component. When this blossoms, its warmth can be a joy to behold – when it turns sour, catastrophe looms. The emotions which make the difference, are not difficult to appreciate – fear, rage and revenge are readily apparent to any who care to look. We must stop treating emotions as if they were some sort of pariah. We need to understand them more clearly – where they come from, how they work. Emotional Health means us controlling them – rather than the other way around.

If you have ever come across a psychiatrist or other doctor who ignored your feelings, or been interviewed by a scientist whose white coat turned them into unemotional aliens – then you need to know that the fault is theirs, not yours. They have been taught that emotions don't matter. Their training is supervised by institutions where discussion of emotion is taboo – defying this ban can hazard your career.

Frozen emotions are the most intriguing. Sometimes childhood memories are too deeply painful to be easily explored – they fester away at the back of the mind. Special measures are called for, as discussed below. Yet even in the most unpromising surroundings, such as Parkhurst Prison, these 'frozen terrors' can still be brought under control – and what works in a maximum security prison can work anywhere. Charlie Bronson's views of my prison work, and Alice Miller's views of this book, are described in their letters, included in the appendix (pages 275 and 277).

Emotional Health

list of chapters

Emotional Health

contents

Introduction

Truth • Frozen Terror • Trust • Consent

'Emotion' – what a deceptively innocent word for something which inflicts such grievous heartaches, havocs and confusions on a long-suffering humanity. Emotions are so slippery that fundamental questions must be settled at the outset. Firstly, what are emotions, and what are they for? Secondly, what is irrationality, and where does it come from? And when Emotional Health finally does arrive, how can you recognise it?

Emotions are certainly odd – easy to feel but impossible to define. Take a look at some of them – fear, anger, guilt, jealousy, rage, joy, delight, gloom, cheerfulness, despair and war – the list is elastic, bewildering and endless. It is elastic because each of these can be expanded sideways – guilt for example, can be described as a mixture of anger and fear. It is bewildering because it tumbles out all higgledy-piggledy, with neither rhyme nor reason nor pattern. And finally it is endless, because there is always another 'emotion' you can tack on to the end. Indeed poets vie with one another to elaborate ever more delicacies of feeling, while the word 'love' has more meanings than there are fish in the sea.

Emotions can make mincemeat of words, befuddle our best intentions, and make a mockery of what we really want. So one thing is clear from the start – misapplied emotions exact a heavy toll. Does the following ring any bells? You get up in the morning, and gloom is already firmly in the driving seat. You struggle to work, only to flounder in a morass of jealousies, bickerings and non-cooperations. Eventually you stumble home to what you always hoped would be a haven of peace, support and recuperation – but somehow that dream dried. Shouldn't life offer more?

The key to tackling this charade is understanding what your emotions get up to, at every point throughout your waking life. Clarity about where emotions are going wrong and confidence in putting them right – these are the basic ingredients of Emotional Health. Every social interaction entails emotional contacts. These can either be benign and bountiful or malign and macerating. The healthier you are emotionally, the more fruitful your social network will be. The more confident you are that your emotions are ringing true, the better equipped you will be to build reliable foundations for what we all aim for – peace of mind. In a nutshell, Emotional Health means growing up emotionally. Easier for some than for others, but richly available to all.

So what are emotions? Well, for one thing they are slippery and fluid, with more possible shapes than a pint of water. They are the most powerful force we ever meet in our lives. Yet they are persistently elusive – the harder you try to define them, the more their 'meaning' slips through your fingers. Emotions cannot be weighed, measured, bottled or counted – thereby causing pandemonium among academics. We need to accept at the outset that there will never be anything equivalent to decibels of rage, nor centilitres of fear. Aches and pains, after all, suffer from exactly the same restrictions, and we cope well enough with them – time to extend a similar courtesy to emotion.

Truth

What makes emotions especially mystifying is the unclear link between words, meanings and feelings. So we need to play them straight. Truth is the first key component of Emotional Health. Indeed Truth is as important here as antisepsis is to a surgeon. When pretence prevails, emotions go berserk with hidden agendas – something at which they excel.

If decibels could measure rage, newborn infants would top the scale. Their 'waaaaaah' stops all other activities in the neighbourhood – they put so much of themselves into it, that it almost seems they might burst a lung. For once, the meaning is crystal-clear. The howls may be entirely wordless, but the message is obvious – 'Don't leave me here, or I'm dead.' If you think I am exaggerating, pick up a newborn infant in full flow. Their tiny body is rigid, they shake with more passion than at any later time, and it consumes their whole being.

Here we see emotions at work. We can readily understand why they are there and what it is they are doing. Indeed this neonatal volcano of emotion shows us a unique pathway through our emotional problems. Perhaps surprisingly, we all know perfectly well what to do to assuage and control exploding emotions in wailing infants. We pick the child up, croon a little, jig gently about, according to taste – in other words we are assuring them that we are present, that we are capable, and that we have their best interests at heart. Our simple task is to convince them that we are not dumping them on the mountainside or anywhere else, to die – not really a heavy drain on our resources. Once reassured, their emotional storm passes.

Now the really curious thing about emotions, and this is something it took me 25 years to untangle, is that this same pattern lies at the heart of every emotional storm. This may seem unlikely – it is certainly not immediately obvious. But the more I explored how emotions work, and where they go so terribly wrong, the more I found that every time, underneath the brouhaha, there was always a misplaced infantile emotion still pulling the strings. No single emotional disease occurs in adult life without its roots being firmly based in the remnants of an infantile strategy – not always easy to see, but invariably there, beneath all the palaver.

The crucial reason this simple underlying pattern remains obscure is that the victim of it is doing their level best to ensure that it does. Our whole adult thrust is to hide these painful 'strategies' at the back of the mind. Indeed it pays us to do so, until we want to do something sensible about it. So not only are emotions the very devil to pin down, but their chief purveyor all too often disguises them, distorts them and colours them differently. No wonder we get in such a stew – hidden agendas destroying so much we hold dear.

Frozen Terror

Let's start with a simple example. Suppose, aged eight, you sing your classmates a song in a foreign language. The response is not applause but laughter. You conclude that your singing is at fault, whereas in fact they were really laughing at the words. Later you might find yourself avoiding all singing events, though you are never very clear as to why you do this. Until the 'hidden fear' is brought out into the open, you sheer away from vocalisings, without ever really understanding what your emotions are doing to you. The point is, you would not dare to begin – the very idea of singing causes you to flee, so the original misperception is never given a chance to be corrected.

How could you ever learn that you had a good singing voice, if you always avoided precisely those situations in which alone, this fact could be revealed? This avoidance would be quite deliberate – who likes being laughed at? What would it take to persuade you to risk facing up to the earlier ridicule, which is the only possible way to discover your misunderstanding? This simple illustration shows the difficulties inherent in all emotional disease. Viewed from the outside, the problem is obvious if not comic – from the inside, it can prove both intractable and tragic. Emotional Education seeks to persuade the victim that today's reality is invariably healthier. In fact, that is all it ever need do.

'Frozen terror', which underlies all serious emotional disorders, always starts in exactly this way. Something happens to the developing child which convinces him or her that further progress along that line of thought will end in disaster. The child says in effect: 'If that's reality, I don't want to know', so they slam the lid on the box and vow never to open it again, on pain of death (or so it seems to them).

When you find adults reacting as if the realities of their nursery still apply, then this is the underlying reason. If instead of using their full capabilities to solve the problems in front of them, they devote their energies to looking around for an echo of a parental figure to do it for them – then this is the underlying cause. What worked, or should have worked, in infancy, is applied willy-nilly in adulthood, where, because things are now different, kindergarten strategies can guarantee only to make matters worse.

Trust

After Truth, the second key component for Emotional Health is Trust. If you cuddle a wailing infant and have not proved trustworthy, your impact is likely to be diminished or worse. Trust is a tricky concept to handle, and indeed to learn. But no human relationship can thrive without it. Even the City of London relies exclusively on Trust – 'my word is my bond'. With Trust so essential for buying and selling, it should be no surprise that it is equally indispensable for ensuring Emotional Health.

Trust is a concept currently in need of repair. Cynics suppose that merchants of all varieties always exploit their customers whenever opportunity allows. But this is a short-term, short-sighted view. Deceits and betrayals command a far wider press, but Trust is indispensable to all social interactions. Perhaps we should start a campaign to demonstrate just how essential and socially responsible Trust is. When you next hurtle down the motorway at lethal speeds, remember you are trusting your fellow drivers not to pull out into your lane, unannounced. You Trust them to be sober, to drive only in the direction of the traffic and to give you fair warning of hold-ups ahead, which they can see and you cannot. Mostly they do.

On occasion, however, Trust is betrayed, and disaster follows. But for the overwhelming majority, Trust proves its social worth. Deceit and betrayal are newsworthy, and can sell many products – Truth and Trust are rarely dramatic, but you cannot be emotionally fit without them.

Consent

To have a foretaste of what Emotional Health is all about, place yourself in the position of that newborn infant. The world around you is strange and blurred – but little different from what you have always known. You can wave your arms and legs about, but cannot lift your head from the pillow. The unsettling notion comes into your mind that these strange giants who feed you sporadically have decided enough is enough and are about to dump you on a deserted doorstep. You do not approve. You do the only thing you have any control over – you yell: 'Waaaaaah.'

When, later, one of these large creatures picks you up and tries to reassure you, you have to decide if they are telling the Truth. That's the first question. Secondly, how trustworthy are they – can you Trust them? Finally, you have to decide whether to accept their offer or not, which brings us to the third key component – do you Consent ? It is up to you to Consent, or to decline. They may coo as much as they please, but you have the inside switch, which you may or may not turn, entirely at your own discretion. Superficially, coercion appears very powerful. But when dealing with matters of the mind there is always the question of whether or not Consent has been sought and obtained. Along with Truth and Trust earlier, Consent is the remaining crucial component of Emotional Health – for all of us, whether infants or adults.

So here we have the three cornerstones of Emotional Health – Truth, Trust and Consent. These are so important to Emotional Health that I elevate them to the status of a basic 'axiom', or fundamental assumption, the implications of which echo throughout the book. Without these three prerequisites the mind becomes a battleground of flailing emotions. In their absence there is not the remotest chance of controlling aberrant emotions, however destructive or even self-destructive they may become. Emotional Health then remains an unattainable pipe dream.

The notion of Consent may seem entirely straightforward. It may seem obvious that you can choose, that valid choices are available to you as of right. Unhappily, psychiatrists today are taught that Consent is an illusion. Along with academic scientists, they are trained to suppose that we all live in a fully determined, Newtonian universe, in which choice and indeed intent are more apparent than real. The risk with this approach of course is that human beings inevitably come to be treated as no more than mindless, unfeeling robots. And where this view prevails, psychiatry is bankrupt.

Can we choose? Can we give Consent ? Or are we bound by rigid wheels of cause and effect? The question is of vital importance. In 1792 Dr Samuel Johnson summed it up succinctly: *'All theory is against the freedom of will; all experience is for it.'* Academic science today, like some latter-day religion, favours believers who profess their faith in the first half of this aphorism, while excommunicating the rest.

Sanity, however, is impossible, unless we deploy choice, intent and some freedom of will. Only by reversing the emphasis can Emotional Health flourish – *'Because all theories are unreliable, it is vital we act responsibly.'*

As we all know, emotions have no difficulty making life hard. But they can also help. Once we corral them, and give them the attention they deserve, we can explore their more positive side. By placing them at the centre of things, where they belong, we can uncover not only better mental health, more robust Emotional Health, but also – something especially welcome in today's gloom – imperishable delights.

Part One:

Basic Emotional Questions

Part One: Basic Emotional Questions

1 What Are Emotions and What Are They for?

Fear – the Master Emotion • Thinking and Feeling • What Emotions Are for

Think back to what you did immediately prior to reading this book. Let's say you walked across the room, dodged round the table and sat in the chair. What could be simpler? Hang on to that simplicity – we need all we can get. Motion is surprisingly complex when you look at it closely.

So the first thing to do is to look at the problems that come just because emotions move things. This helps to distinguish these initial difficulties from those unfathomable mysteries that emotions bring along with them anyway.

You walked or moved from A to B, from one side of the room to the other. For the moment, we won't ask why, though this is in fact the only possible solution. Suppose you tried to describe, scientifically, what you actually did. First of all you would have to define where A was, then the same for B. How accurate do you want to be? Nowadays we have satellite navigation systems that can pinpoint your two positions with metre, even millimetre, accuracy, should you need it, so you might think defining where A and B actually are has been solved.

Then when describing motion, we need a measure of speed. Speed is defined as distance travelled per unit time – miles per hour, metres per minute, or, in the case of light, kilometres per second. It sounds simple, but in practical reality it has proved utterly bewildering – it took Einstein to 'solve' the problem of the speed of light, and he did so only at the cost of shedding Newtonian physics for ever. Note that this is the most universal, objective, scientific measurement that we can possibly muster – and there is an unsolved mystery at its very heart – why is the speed of light 'constant'? This is one fundamental question among innumerable others that academic science cannot even come close to answering.

Describing moving from there to here is far from straightforward, yet worse is to come. We still have the question of timing – when did you start and when did you finish? Do you want Universal Time, Greenwich Mean Time or British Summer Time? Are you working to the Gregorian Calendar, the Eastern Orthodox Calendar or one of your own preference? Does time seem to pass slower for you because you are younger, or quicker as you age?   Einstein even had the temerity to suppose that time slowed as you travelled faster – can you credit that ? If, like one earlier editor of this book, you take comfort from the notion that Einstein merely adjusted Newton's view in minor details, then try having the subtleties of the 'relativity of simultaneity' explained – that slew of polysyllables divests the everyday notion of 'now' of any residual scientific merit.

Describing a relatively simple movement such as walking from A to B, in absolute objective, 'scientific' terms, can prove overwhelmingly difficult. And this for something you can see clearly enough, and which everyone else can understand, at least in principle. It gets worse still when we come to moving around inside your mind. The table you dodged round to get to where you are now reading this page has its counterpart in your mind, along with a host of other mental furniture, some of which is a great deal less obvious.

But here's the exciting part – your emotions move that furniture around. Indeed that is what they are for. If your emotions are clear and straightforward, you can tidy all your mental items into a coherent order and set about doing what you wanted to do in the first place. If, on the other hand, you can only see things unclearly and your self-confidence is low, your emotions can wreak enough havoc for a lifetime. It happens.

So what is the most reliable way to describe what you did immediately prior to reading this page? Why not say: 'I crossed the room because I intended to read the book.' This involves the use of an even more mysterious notion – intent. But adding another mystery to the first can sometimes give a more intelligible result than either on its own. Don't ask me why or how.

Fear – the Master Emotion

The first rule when considering any feature of human beings, whether emotions, intentions or indeed hearts and lungs, is always to remember that these items are all parts of a single whole. We may talk of different bits and pieces as if they were independent items, but that is merely for our verbal convenience. So while we are ostensibly talking about emotions as though they were discrete entities, in fact you never have a human emotion by itself. In practice they simply don't exist in the absence of a conscious living human being – quite a thought.

So instead of trying to divide emotions into separate pigeonholes, let's take a more practical approach. Let's start by asking what do all emotions do? Well, they move your mental furniture. And on occasion, especially on exciting occasions, they move you faster than you are accustomed to go. The word 'emotion' consists more of 'motion' than anything else – indeed people will often say: 'I was very moved', meaning they became emotional.

But we need to go further. One crucial insight that helped me here came from one of my youngest clients, a boy of about six. I saw him regularly for a matter of weeks, when he was having unusually difficult times at primary school. As always, I would start each session by asking him what it was we talked about last time and which bits helped and which didn't. His response was so clear, so typical of the young. We talked, he said, about the 'nice and nasties'. Here, in a nutshell, is the way to get a handle on our otherwise anarchic emotions.

Instead of struggling to define what all the different emotions are, we merely slot them roughly into place on a scale or continuum, from benign to malign, good to bad, positive to negative, 'nice' or 'nasty'. With a bit of practice each emotion we encounter can be allocated into one of two baskets – positive emotions or negative ones. At the negative end are fear and rage. At the positive, delight and joy. It's not entirely watertight, but remarkably useful in practice. And by freeing us from the morass of defining details, it allows us to concentrate on how they work out in practical reality, and ultimately to begin to draw up sensible and reliable foundations for Emotional Health.

And the end that matters most when it comes to Emotional Health is the 'heavy' end. If I could have only one emotion out of the full range to work with, the one I would unhesitatingly choose, and the one that proves most fruitful when dealing with all emotional tangles, irrationalities and other savage mental disorders, is fear. Fear is the master emotion. When fear is abroad, all the happy, sunny emotions flee. Big fear earns the label 'terror'. Fear can do what no other emotion can – paralyse thought. And if Homo sapiens suffers thought paralysis, death and extinction loom.

Further, by corralling emotions into one long line – goodies at one end and baddies at the other – we can at last give some objective legitimacy to the happy end, to joy. Just as I would never presume to tell one of my medical customers what type of pain they were suffering from, nor indeed what variety of emotion, so I would not presume to describe how they might experience joy. However, I will say this – what I learnt from exploring the emotions of the most dangerous and violent men in the British prison system is that every one of us is born Lovable, Sociable and Non-violent. And, deep down, that is where we want to return. If you can peel off all the exterior detritus, all the hard, ingrained grime of fear, of deceit, of coercion – then beneath it all you will find the true vessel of joy. This again is so fundamental that it forms the second axiom or basic assumption, – Lovable, Sociable and Non-Violent – to which later chapters return. More obvious in some, less in others – but assuredly available to all.

Thinking and Feeling

Thoughts and thinking are utterly mysterious – fascinating when they work, frustrating or worse when they don't – but quite impossible to know in 100 per cent detail. We are scratching with a broken fingernail at the surface of a vast, unknowable iceberg. No wonder we have to feel our way, gingerly and loaded with ignorance.

So what is it that promotes the flow of thoughts, or indeed of words, through our minds? This is the motion we considered earlier – the simple answer is emotion. It has to be simple, because the reality is that we have absolutely no idea, nor any possible means of gaining the least conception of what this flow, of what this motion, is all about.

In practical terms, our working definition of emotion is something which moves our mental furniture. Our trains of thought are moved along, partly by 'motion' and partly by rationality. In other words, partly by feelings and partly by apparent reasonableness, at least in principle.

I like to link the motion of our thoughts with the motion of all other parts of our bodies. I have no idea why a living organism moves and a dead one does not. The two are composed of entirely the same chemicals, sub-atomic particles and other imponderables, but whereas the one moves, the other decidedly does not. It is because we are alive that we have emotions, and it is these which move us from time to time. Not only do they move us, but we need to improve the way they do so – in other words, build a reliable pathway to Emotional Health.

Just as it is clear there are never any emotions without living organisms for them to exist in, so there is no such thing as a thoughtless emotion nor yet an emotionless thought. Obviously there are times when the one element is less conspicuous than the other, especially in desperation, and when terror and panic are abroad. But in principle the two go inextricably together.

This is not really surprising if we come out of the unclear and essentially intangible world of mental furniture and look at what happens out on the street. There we see vehicles moving about all over the place, except when gridlocked. We don't spend hours cogitating on how moving cars differ from non-moving. We assume cars move – that is what they are designed to do, so this isn't a problem. So neither should it be for our mental apparatus – our emotions move because that is what they do and are, by definition. They propel our thoughts, which is what they are for. However, as we are aiming for Emotional Health, the objective is to increase the thought component so as to have a clearer idea of where our emotions are striving to move us, and why. In a nutshell, by thinking more clearly about them, our emotions become healthier.

What Emotions Are for

Emotions are life-saving. Emotions are entirely impervious to definition – the route to ever-greater verbal precision is doomed to fail. Emotions, in reality, have an infinite number of aliases, but only one function – saving lives. And, in practice, this is all we really need to know about their 'essence', their intrinsic nature. They exist as an integral part of living organisms and their primary purpose or function is to save life. The original purpose of fear, for example, is to protect the individual from a danger that could be life-threatening. If you have no fear of walking across busy motorway traffic, you risk becoming legless. If you have no fear of walking across the Sahara without water, your perambulations will be brief.

The nearest analogy is with bodily pain. Pain is always unpleasant, or worse. That is its purpose. If you felt no pain when your hand was in the flame, you would soon end up with a stump. Exactly the same applies to fear. You may think ahead and suspect that there is a tiger in the next room, but if you have no fear, you risk becoming breakfast. There is nothing wrong with a realistic fear – unlike an unrealistic or irrational fear. If you spent the rest of life believing there was a tiger next door and there never was – the costs in terms of a misspent life are huge.

The remedy for any fear, rational or irrational, is to find where it is coming from and remove the danger it portends. This may be relatively easy in a stable, well-knit society, where we all cooperate together to help build our joint communal security. However, it is less easy when strife threatens or when the cause of the fear, though real enough at the time, is now lost in the mists of the past, from which it has become too painful to re-evaluate and remove.

Anger, like pain, is a healthy emotion – though this is something that too many of my customers have the greatest difficulty in learning. To illustrate this, I encourage them to shout at, for example, the milkman. When I was a lad, the milkman used to make daily deliveries. Suppose you asked for two pints a day and he or she kept bringing ten. After a while you would say: 'Hey, just a minute, I asked for two. You bring ten. What's going on?' If you are not angry, have never been angry and are not allowed by all your training to be angry, then, before you utter a peep, your house is full of rotting milk.

Again, anger is only healthy when directed at the source of the problem. When it becomes 'free-floating' or adrift, then the last person who deserves it is liable to catch it. Unrealistic anger, as for any other emotion, is always irrational. Shouting at the cat, or some other innocent, because you daren't shout at the true source of the trouble, can be very unhealthy indeed. And however healthy anger may be, coercive violence never is.

So the elements of Emotional Health that we need to emphasize here are the ability to distinguish realistic fear and anger from irrational and unrealistic emotions. Anger is somewhat subordinate to fear – <u>you cannot be angry unless you are a little afraid</u> – just as you might try shouting at the tiger, hoping to drive it off, before fear kicks in and forces you to flee.

If you watch nature documentaries of undersea life, you will see that sharks and other predators hear underwater sounds from some distance and come over to see what the disturbance is. Any vibrations out of the ordinary attract a crowd. The same is true for life in the street. You may suddenly hear raised voices or shouts as from a fracas. These are non-verbal social communications, essentially emotional signals, to which we can all react.

Conversely, we can respond equally well to situations and contexts which have been marked 'good'. Just as some animals spray parts of their territory so that others know the boundaries – so we, as highly Sociable animals, have developed a device whereby we can let our fellows know that such and such is worth pursuing and is generally safe and benign.

This allows us to colour the murk that otherwise surrounds us. Watch someone describing an event they enjoyed – their face is animated, their speech lively, their gestures energetic. They are labelling something we are unfamiliar with as 'good' rather than as 'bad', 'better' rather than 'worse'. We too can benefit from this, provided we apply the first axiom – Truth, Trust and Consent – in full measure.

The long induction we all receive as children consists of precisely this sort of emotional tagging – certain items receive parental approval, whereas others are decidedly dubious, if not downright taboo. Not all of these markings are helpful and realistic – sorting the one from the other is a sure sign of emotional maturity, not to say Emotional Health. Some learn that we are born hateful, anti-social and violent – so it may take a while before the healthier approach advocated by the second axiom can hold more fruitful sway.

Emotional Health depends on our fellow humans revealing their deeper nature, namely that they really are Lovable, Sociable and Non-Violent. Our social and indeed emotional success depends on ascertaining just how True this axiom is.

2 What Is an Irrational Emotion and What Goes Wrong?

Always Maximum and Always Obsolete • The Mental Landmine and the Area around It

An irrational emotion is indistinguishable from any other. If you believed there was a tiger behind the sofa it would make no difference whether the tiger was real or imaginary. This is the whole issue in a nutshell. You cannot tell, just by looking, whether an emotion is real or irrational – the effect on the individual is the same.

It will be obvious just how important Truth, Trust and Consent are in such a context. If the victim does not believe you are telling the Truth, and does not Trust you with their life, they won't Consent to accept your reassurance.

If there is insufficient Truth, Trust and Consent available, the victim of the irrational emotion will strenuously decline to examine the cause of the irrationality, which thereafter takes on a life of its own. You may resent this constant cry of 'Wolf, wolf' or 'Tiger, tiger', but your resentment will do nothing to help the irrational terror subside. The only thing that can do this is certainty on the part of the victim that the threat, the original source of the terror, has gone. And this only occurs when the individual Consents to re-evaluate the original threat and allows it to slip back into the long-distant past, which is where it first originated, and where it now belongs. Only in this way can 'frozen terror' be melted.

Terror paralyses the mind. If you are reading this in a warm, cosy room in which all is peaceful and calm, try a little thought experiment. Imagine you are in a stateroom on a grand ocean liner, cruising somewhere luxurious. Gripped by the revelations on every page, you little notice that the engine-room hum has stopped and the liner has come to a standstill in mid-ocean. Under the door seeps a tell-tale trickle of sea water, to which you remain oblivious. Steadily the seepage becomes a flood. Through the portholes, water can now be seen rising. You scarcely register that the floor and the ceiling have assumed an unusual angle, rather less horizontal than is customary.

Someone screams. Suddenly you know the ship is sinking. The room rapidly begins to fill with water. Death by drowning stares you in the face. Do you think logically? Does your penchant for calm, reasoned argument remain uppermost in your mind? Faced with certain death, most of us would do almost anything to avoid it. We would scrabble for the only remaining exit. We would not stop to reason things out – we panic.

In this context, sensible reasoning is stillborn – if you delay, you are dead. It would appear entirely rational not to delay, but to act first and think later. An assured casualty of this 'streamlining' approach is realistic thinking.

The human mind is not equipped to think clearly when terrified. This is a fact of life. And yet, of course, rational thought is precisely what is needed to defeat an irrational emotion. It is like sitting in a First World War foxhole. You have no way of knowing the danger is passed, except by putting your head out into the open. Since you have been well trained that that will get it blown off – a vicious, and unbreakable circle is set up. Calm, reasoned argument, with multiple and ceaseless reassurance, might eventually persuade you to risk what you have known up to that point is certain death – but even then it could be touch and go.

Always Maximum and Always Obsolete

Irrational emotions bear no relation to present circumstances. Irrational emotions occur and persist in individuals who have at some time in their past been so terrified that they rule out any possibility of rethinking the pain which caused the problem in the first place. The human mind chooses to disable itself. Whereas most human problems are resolved through active consideration – here is one which is too toxic even to be thought about. Terror paralyses the capacity for rational thought – and where there is no rational thought, irrationality blooms.

This is a highly charged area, requiring great expertise. Three times while working in Parkhurst Prison my life was threatened by murderers who found my enquiries too painful. So while 'frozen terrors' may appear obviously illogical to you, it is vital to take care when trying to unpack them. They were established in an era when, for that individual, life and death hung in the balance. If you tread too clumsily, this same balance may tip against you.

The curious thing about irrationality is that the victim of it is comprehensively ignorant of it. They complain hugely about peripheral matters, while ignoring anything that impacts on the root of the problem. After several decades it was this 'active' ignorance which provided the key. The ignorance is not casual, not happenchance – it is, in a bizarre way, wilful, even deliberate.

The clue to understanding irrationality, and thence Emotional Health, lies in the very size of the irrational emotions. In every case today's irrational emotions are as huge as the emotions which did once exist for real within that individual, when they were infants and could do nothing about it. Deeply buried within the individual there is a real pain, a real agony, which that individual will do anything to keep hidden. They cope today by pretending the terror isn't there, that it doesn't exist and it doesn't really hurt at all.

What could be more important than ridding yourself of all these painful irrationalities – bearing in mind that these irrational emotions can seriously curtail your life, even finally ending it in suicide? The key that emerged was that this higher priority was indeed life-threatening – but from an earlier era. Clearly Consent is here stretched to the limit by the challenge of persuading the individual to look at the last thing they wish to see.

Sigmund Freud illustrates the point. Here we have one of the sharpest medical observers of the past two or three centuries, a man so powerful he unhappily bestrides the bulk of twentieth-century thinking on what human beings are really like. And yet his whole edifice is shot through with contradictions, irrationalities and unrealities – Freudian theory is, in a word, bunk.

Aged 80, he describes his fear of his father, claiming that we should all be afraid of them – fathers, that is. And the terrifying event which underlay this residual infantile terror is described explicitly in his Interpretation of Dreams, where, aged 'seven or eight', he describes his father bellowing at him: '*The boy will come to nothing.*' Sadly for us all, he was dancing to two tunes – the first was the clinical need to wrestle with the quantities of vile and destructive irrational emotion – the second was to 'prove' somehow to a long-deceased father that he had amounted to something.

Of course, if we have an anxious parent, it is entirely understandable that their anxieties should become built into our 'personalities' along with all the other infantile training which is so essential to our development. But the key to the problem is to appreciate, as Freud did not, that there is a resolution to the dilemma. Parents are only human. They make mistakes as we all do. But if we are emotionally mature, we can pick and choose those mistakes we wish to retain as our own pet prejudices and those we most sensibly wish to discard. And the more adept we become at this, the healthier we are emotionally.

The Mental Landmine and the Area around It

What can go so wrong, that a genius of such brilliance and promise as Freud can end up doing more harm than good? The reason is simple, but actively obscured. The more articulate you are and the more powerful your mental resources, the more effectively can you hide your real fearful emotions away, even from yourself. The victim does not want to know the real root of his emotions – and works as hard as he or she possibly can to make sure that this pseudo-ignorance remains intact, on pain of death. The threat to their life has long since past – in reality, but not in their perceptions – whence 'frozen terror'.

The clearest example of what goes wrong was shown me by one of my youngest customers. Sam was only seven and a half. He had spindly legs and chattered away 19 to the dozen. He stuffed his hand in his mouth from time to time, as boys of that age do when shy. And he couldn't stop talking. However, I asked him one question which staunched the verbal flow 100 per cent – and showed precisely what had gone wrong.

I had been treating Sam's mother for a serious self-harming disease where, when frustrated, she would bang her head against the wall or bite her own hand savagely. She had done very well – we had traced her rage back to its infantile source. She had faced it, vented it and was about to be discharged. She had been 'bite-free' for over six months by then, knew where these 'tantrums' came from and how to rid herself of them permanently.

As we came to agree the final session she paused and mentioned that her son was inflicting problems on the harmonious running of the family home. In the mornings he

Part One: Basic Emotional Questions

would take over an hour to get dressed, endlessly shuffling through which sock to put on – thus effectively delaying his smooth progression towards school. She was at her wits' end and asked if I would see Sam. I suggested we made one further appointment, not for her, but for him, so we could see what could be done.

Now sock syndromes in seven-year-old schoolboys had hardly been my speciality at that juncture, having had more experience of dealing with death threats from serial killers and unpacking the problems behind paedophilia. But I reasoned that human minds, and especially human thought patterns, had enormous amounts in common, especially when they went wrong. Perhaps I could learn something further.

So Sam arrived. He sat in the armchair I reserved for my clients, with his mother behind him. My first dilemma, apart from not having the remotest idea what sock selection had to do with anything, was to find out if his mother was in fact the source of the 'frozen terror' I was relying on being there. If she was, it seemed unlikely that Sam would discuss the problem with his mother so physically close and so obviously to the fore. I therefore invited Sam to agree that we ask his mother to sit outside, trying as I did so to detect a hesitation, a glimmer of fear, that clung to his internal picture of his mother. Nothing. It had clearly never entered Sam's head that his mother would sit outside, so on we went with her there. I supposed in a general sort of way that it might therefore be something to do with his father – but as yet there was no evidence either way.

We chatted on about his school, his home life, his family. I was looking, as I invariably do, for fear and anger from his earlier childhood. Again nothing. What was I, an adult psychiatrist, doing exploring the inside of a child's mind? I tried a different tack. Sometimes, by catching the individual somewhat off guard, looking the other way, it is possible to glimpse where the real problem is, where the real 'landmine' is lurking. I came up with the following.

2 What Is an Irrational Emotion and What Goes Wrong?   25

'Now, Sam, when your mother bit herself, you were frightened?' I asked this half as a suggestion, half as a question expecting the answer 'yes'. I asked it in as gentle a manner as possible – no pressure, no threats, just ever so matter of fact. But I was also quite firm – there was no way this question was an aside, nor could it be ignored. Sam responded vigorously – it was clear that, at last, we were on the right track. But he responded entirely non-verbally. His jaw dropped. No words passed his lips, which in such a chatterbox was quite an event.

He did, however, nod his head frantically. Again I needed to spring a surprise. I said, 'What did I say, Sam?' And it was then the 'frozen terror' stood revealed. Sam struggled with himself, he relocated his jaw, found his tongue and used it to totally obstructive effect: 'I forget,' he said.

The mental landmine in Sam's case was the terror he had experienced when his mother, his essential life-support system, began attacking either the wall, or her own hands. Her irrational 'tantrums' inevitably put his life on the line. Landmines explode unexpectedly – therefore any approach to the area around the landmine is vigorously resisted, using every available item, weapon or thought pattern. If you are a murderer, you threaten to murder so as to prevent the landmine being inadvertently approached and thereby exploded. If you are the father of psychoanalysis, you invent dreams, symbols and fantasies – and you do so to avoid all possibility that parents may, in some circumstances, however limited, be talked of as abusive.

In Sam's case I didn't know where the landmine was – but I did know there was a landmine which was radiating such toxic feelings that family life was becoming intolerable. The only person who did, expressly did not want either to know, still less to tell me. So far as Sam knew, no one could discuss these horrific scenes and live. My first essential task was to try and convince this seven-and-a-half-year-old that it was safe. I, together with his mother, needed to bring about a context in which dying by sudden explosive emotions was not going to happen. The evidence that Sam thought it was, is clear from the total cessation of his mind. He believed that if he thought about his mother biting herself, his life was at stake – and he was determined not to risk it – whence the cessation of his thought processes.

Earlier I discussed emotionless thought and how this is a practical impossibility. Here is an instance where all the emotions leave the scene, so there is nothing left to inch the thinking forwards. It is like a small boat sailing along, when suddenly the wind drops and forward progression is no more – you can rattle the boom or jiggle the tiller – but the power has gone out of the sail and willy-nilly you are stationary. In the absence of sensible emotions, sensible reasoning evaporates.

So when Sam asked me to believe that he had 'forgotten' the most important emotional event in his young life – what he really meant was that if he proceeded any further down the avenue I had invited him along, the landmine would explode and he would be no more. Rather than this, he preferred to shut down his central thinking processor – which he did. Obviously what was needed was to convince him that the landmine was now a dud.

The area around the landmine is crucial. It is a no-man's land fenced off with as robust a fencing as that individual can muster. And the stronger the mental equipment, the more needs to be dismantled, not from the outside by coercion, but from the inside by a supported, trusting individual, who finally gives the whole healthy operation his wholehearted Consent. Without this, you are whistling in the wind.

So this is why the problem is so potent – the human mind is crippling itself to avoid what it perceives as a fatal scenario. I repeated: 'When your mother bit herself, you were frightened.' I then gently asked Sam again what it was I had said. He could no longer say he had forgotten – I was quite clearly set to continue repeating the phrase until the cows came home, so the 'forgotten' ploy would not work a second time.

And then he did something he never dreamt he would ever do, and live. He began, hesitantly at first, to repeat the unthinkable, to send out feelers into the area marked CERTAIN DEATH IF YOU ENTER THIS SPOT. As he did so, his face brightened and his hesitancy faded. The world did not come to an end. His mother did not turn into some ravenous beast and eat everything in sight. No, he had driven a pathway through his no-go area and the landmine did not explode. He could now get on with the rest of his life.

This is the key to Emotional Health – thinking and voicing your frozen fears does not necessarily bring death – it can, in today's reality, save your life.

3 What Are Healthy Emotions and What Is Emotional Health?

Reasonable Fears and Reasonable Angers • Invisible Hazards • Emotional Idylls

The single-scale approach, with negative emotions at one end and positive cheerful ones at the other, is a great practical help, since it allows us to assess every emotion by how much negativity or positivity it has. This is remarkably useful. In particular, it avoids being tied down to saying precisely what emotions are – we feel them, but defining them is impossible. So here's another rule of thumb – emotions are strongest in infancy, but they gradually become less powerful as we grow older. This is not to say that the elderly do not become animated, or feel matters powerfully – certainly they do. But it does mean that the intensity, the sheer 'waaaaaah' of the newborn infant, becomes steadily more moderated as we get older – or at least it should.

This should not be surprising. Given that our emotions are part of our life-saving systems, we would anticipate that they should change as our lives, especially our physical lives, become more secure and we become correspondingly more capable. Neonates cannot even lift their heads from the pillow, whereas youths can make themselves useful about the house, help with the household chores and gradually prepare for the time when they too will have a home of their own.

As we move along the developmental trail we steadily acquire the ability to look after ourselves. We gradually bring under our own control such life necessities as a roof over our heads and a regular supply of vitals. And as we do so, the risks recede. Accordingly, if I now come across an emotion that is exceptionally powerful or unusually 'blind', I instantly label it 'infantile'. In other words, it indicates that this adult has become stuck in an earlier phase of their development. Rage and terror, and indeed violence when found in adults, fall straight into this category. The intensity is no longer appropriate.

Or look at the matter another way – if you are frightened of something, you would expect to acknowledge it, act upon it, reduce and eventually (if it was within your power to do so) eliminate it altogether. Say you were frightened of the cold – why then you would set about acquiring adequate supplies of warm clothing, enough insulation in the living quarters and a steady supply of, if not fossil fuel, solar or wind power. In other words, reasonable fears have entirely reasonable remedies – what is the point of being intelligent, cooperative human beings if we cannot solve the practical problems which our environment throws in our direction. By all means register the fear – but take a hard look at it, evaluate its fuller implications and get on with the task of removing the root cause. This may sound obvious, but exactly the same strategy applies to the irrational emotions and irrational behaviours, as Sam showed earlier.

Reasonable Fears and Reasonable Angers

Fear, of course, is the master emotion; it is the one which, when it pulls the strings, makes all the others jump. Anger is the noisy emotion. But what applies to fear applies equally well to anger. It is always worth giving the tiger a good bellow – there is just the chance that, with a big enough song and dance, the man-eating monster may decide to look elsewhere for breakfast. So while fear is at the most negative end of our emotional spectrum, anger is situated just one pip in from the end and is therefore subordinate to it. Anger is not quite so reliable in protecting your life – you may still have to flee. In practice, I have found it helpful always to look for the sliver of fear that lurks beneath the noise. Indeed in the total absence of fear there is simply no call for anger, which vaporizes.

Anger itself brings a whole range of awesome problems – later chapters include examples of how it goes so painfully awry. But the real problem with anger is that so many of my clients are not allowed to have it at all. In their book 'reasonable anger' is a contradiction in terms. This leads to all manner of problems. I was recently responsible for a women's unit, where 90 per cent harmed themselves. Discussing anger with them was most instructive. One 20-year-old coined a beautiful phrase for me – 'trapped anger'. What this signifies is that anger induced by a series of injustices becomes all bottled up inside, such that its only way out lies in self-harm, self-strangulation, self-starvation.

The remedy consists of ventilating this anger, to give it expression and to target it in the general direction of the abuser. I would regularly encourage my customers to shout at a figment of their abuser – something which initially was entirely impossible for them to do. Just as Sam could not think when discussing his fear, so, in these cases too, the mind shuts down. They were still terrified of what would have happened had they expressed even the first hint of their entirely justified anger, in the context of their earlier terrifying abuse. In one instance I had the greatest difficulty in persuading my client to visualize her abuser, let alone shout at him. Initially she could only see his boots, later his knees and so on, until eventually she could meet his eye and give him a full blast of her distress. When she had done so, the whole episode lost its power, taking her symptoms with it.

I should emphasize that the above confrontation was entirely in role play. My customer was addressing an empty chair – the real individual would have been far too terrifying. Moreover, the important point is not to be angry with the individual today, but to learn to express the bottled anger from the past. Sam could not, initially, say he was frightened of his mother. Similarly, too many cannot say they are angry at the injustices they have experienced or perceive themselves to have experienced. When they can, they become sane.

We may deplore the existence of negative emotion, we may feel that anger is not a civilized commodity to have. Yet the reality is that anger does occur, just as pain does. You can pretend it doesn't, or shouldn't be there. Yet all the time it thrashes around and inflicts enormous damage. Trapped anger is highly toxic.

The remedy, just as with reasonable fears, is not to shut your eyes to the fact that these powerful entities are out there, but rather to find where the anger is coming from and deal with that at source. In that way we can hitch ourselves up one notch in the 'mature civilized' stakes and inch our way towards Emotional Health.

Invisible Hazards

Here's another thought experiment. There is a powerful, shapeless force which from time to time sweeps through a community, inflicting great destruction. Houses and homes are torn apart and people are killed at random. Suppose that the force or entity behind this particular destruction is invisible. It can only be detected by humans from the impact it has on other, more visible things. Would this be enough for us to wash our hands of it – saying there was nothing we could do? What if we concluded that it really was far too vague and amorphous for us even to discuss it sensibly? No. Just because this particular agency was invisible would never exempt it from intense human scrutiny, analysis and action. This force shows itself only by the effect it has on tangible things – it is the wind.

Yet, although the wind itself is invisible, we prepare weather maps, construct wind-resistant housing, move whole communities out of reach of hurricanes and batten down hatches generally. The fact that the hurricane is invisible does nothing to remove it from our sphere of action. So why can't we do something entirely equivalent for emotional storms? Even though emotions can never be measured – this is not a serious drawback in practice. Just as we feel the wind – so we also feel emotions, whether our own or others'. If a meteorologist said he or she could do nothing, on account of an inability to see or define the shape of the wind – your response would be ridicule. If a psychiatrist said precisely the same about emotions, perhaps a touch more in the way of outrage would be in order.

The weather gives us a further insight into emotions. When airline pilots describe flight paths they sometimes refer to a patch of 'weather' ahead. In other words, the norm is clear blue sunlight – weather is when something interferes with this peace and calm. This is really what Emotional Health is about. When the storms and cyclones abate, then warm, sunny emotions can prevail – and they do.

 The Japanese have a concept of inner harmony, or 'Wa', which those around them have an obligation to respect and bolster. This is another description of the same point. Inside each of us is the capability of spinning anew all sorts of delights, cheers, happinesses – indeed all manner of positive emotions. We don't have to earn this, or be born into the right social strata – no, this is simply part of what it means to be a sentient feeling human being. We have emotions, and if we can cultivate and cherish them (and each other) they can blossom and fructify, just because that's what living human emotions are all about.

Emotional Idylls

How would you picture an idyll? Let's try and give Emotional Health a concrete description. Picture a sunny day; there's a gentle breeze; lambs gambol in the meadow; the baby is cooing peacefully at a small blue butterfly flitting around the brightly coloured coverlet. Your partner passes through, brimming with contentment and bonhomie; the mortgage is paid; money is coming through for those little non-essentials – you even have a moment to breathe a happy sigh of contentment and contemplate future delights.

Does this ring any bells? Or do you feel it is too unrealistic for you? Too many of my clients arrive in adult life convinced that they are worse than useless, that the world is a grim and difficult place and there is nothing realistic they can do to change things.

However, if we were discussing physical fitness you would not doubt that you could improve your physical capability. Even if you could only manage a few steps or a few minutes' exercise without becoming breathless, you would believe that by working steadily at it you could increase your physical capacities.

Why is it so hard for us to apply similar reasoning to emotional or mental health? Why assume that, because your experience of mental agility has up to now been negative, that this is how it must always be?   What steps would be needed to change your mind?

First, we need to establish the Truth of the matter – can human beings be happy?   A number of people, including myself, declare this to be the case. It could be argued that if it is possible for some human beings, then, in principle, it is possible for all.

There is another aspect of Truth that needs to be considered here. My working definition of Truth is the degree to which

34   *Emotional Idylls*

your mental furniture faithfully reflects the real world. It is a measure of the correlation with reality. Thus it is more true to say that the world is round than flat – an important consideration for global circumnavigators.

Truth is a relative measure of how closely what you think and believe matches up to what is really out there. Truth can never now be absolute. There will always be a discrepancy between the two. But just as there will always be some ill health lurking about – that does not mean we should not aspire to both good health and better Truthfulness.

The next step is – why are you so gloomy? Generally this can be accounted for by the experiences you have had so far. If those in charge of your early years, and those who have added to your experience since, have universally taken a negative view of humanity, what chance have you to think, feel or believe differently?

However, if training can lead firstly in one direction, it is equally capable of leading in another, such that you can learn an optimistic, positive view. The important point here is to avoid self-deception. Truth invariably means being more realistic, not less. If it's not true for you, don't buy it.

The first Truth about Emotional Health is that we are all born Lovable. Newborn infants are 100 per cent Lovable – why shouldn't this 'lovability' persist throughout life? If you find yourself saying that it didn't for you, we need to find out where the 'lovability' went. There are cynics, of course, including even some theologians who should know better, who fiercely maintain that we are all born evil and decidedly unlovable. This is not what I found to be the case in the most unlikely spot imaginable – the deepest dungeon of the prison system. My Parkhurst Prison customers proved beyond doubt that they had not been born hateful, and given half a chance, they would revert to being Lovable, which they much preferred anyway. Strange but true.

Next, if it is true, as I obviously believe, that every human being is born Lovable – can you trust me?   Well, obviously it depends on how trustworthy you find me, how much weight you place on the Truth of what I say, how much you can rely on my account of the matter rather than anyone else's, including your own.

Trust needs to be set in a wider context too. As Sociable animals we need to work together to limit the risks and insecurities which the harsh inanimate world holds in store for all living organisms. The example of the tiger helps. Suppose I am further down the road than you, so that I can see round the next bend, where you cannot. I make a careful exploration and send you the good news that there is no tiger there. You cannot see for yourself, you have only my word for it. Do you Trust me?

Clearly you will be able to judge this issue better by looking at my past history. Have I given accurate reports in the past?   If your subsequent experiences bear out what I say, my degree of trustworthiness will grow, and it will become less of an issue whether you can bring yourself to Trust me. What is needed is continual and responsible vigilance on both sides, but with practice it is achievable.

Fundamentally, we are a Sociable species, and Trust is a crucial element in our survival, certainly in our happier survival. Look at our commercial activities – Trust there is invaluable. We accept dirty bits of paper and odiferous coinage in exchange for something we have worked hard for. If we lose Trust in our currency, we face social ruin. Precisely the same applies to Emotional Health – Trust is indispensable. Indeed the only cure for a fear you cannot see is the trusty support of someone who can. If you cannot get to the next bend, you will never know if a tiger is there. Only by trusting the advanced guard have you any hope of assuaging your terror of tigers, or of anything else.

Human beings are born Lovable and Sociable. The fact that we are also born Non-violent may not be immediately obvious. For me it is axiomatic that we are all born Lovable, Sociable and Non-violent – and furthermore, that underneath all our protestations to the contrary, we are this way, or deep down would wish to be this way, throughout our lives. More – as we become emotionally fitter, so we need to rely less and less on coercion, which includes violence. Violence in my experience is a disease. It is a learned disease. And it can be unlearned. As we become Emotionally Fitter, these three components, with which everyone of us is born, come ever more to the fore. But perhaps for now this assertion may not receive your Consent.

Consent itself is an intriguing concept, which is not at all easy to grasp. Coercion and violence are so commonplace that the vital importance of Consent can be overlooked. There are two ways of getting what you want. You can force the issue, or you can obtain Consent. If you want cheese and your vendor tries to force you to buy chalk, what or who decides the outcome? If your vendor is bigger than you and has half a dozen men-at-arms to impose his or her will, conventional wisdom says that you will lose. But will you?

If there are six of them and one of you, and they want to sit on your head, there is precious little you can do at first to stop them. But if they want to remain your friend, if they have even the remotest inkling that you might conceivably be a customer, even only a haphazard one – the last thing they will want to do is coerce you.

So what is the issue here? Preconceptions about being virile or macho muddy the picture – what is needed is calm inspection. You want cheese, your merchant wants to sell chalk – in the real world there is no contest. The customer wins. And the reason for this is simple – if he or she does not, the customer evaporates – there are no customers. A customer by definition is someone who wants something – the customer decides what it is they want, when they want it, and on their Consent, and on that alone, does the transaction go through. Every successful merchant know this – there are endless schemes for beguiling the customer – none for coercing her or him.

What connection is there between what happens in everyday commercial life and what we would like to happen in our emotional life?   If the connection is close, it follows that Consent must play a large part in improving that life. If you want gentle emotions supporting your fears and your wants, give as much priority to obtaining Consent as any merchant would. Things done by Consent are infinitely more enduring and reliable than anything coercion can ever achieve. Harder to get, but much more fruitful when you get there.

If you think Consent is intriguing and difficult to understand, you should meet its cousin – intent – which is even more so. Like emotions, it cannot be measured or even very clearly defined. Intent so resists comprehension that contemporary psychiatry and most of academic science discards it altogether – an omission that would certainly suffocate the practice of law, much as it already has the practice of psychiatry.

We have anemometers to measure the wind, but there are no emotionometers to measure emotions. So do we pack up and go home? Or do we do the best we can with what we have got and feel our way to a more secure emotional environment, and thence to Emotional Health? Emotions have been omitted from psychiatric consideration because they are impossible to define. Place them centre-stage, where they belong, and then at last Emotional Health can open up whole new vistas of unending delights, not for the chosen few, the privileged elite, but for all.

Part Two –

Problems Within Yourself

Part Two –Problems Within Yourself

4 Why Your Mind Stops You Doing What You Want

The Invisible Roadblock • Opening the Box and Tidying Your Mind • 'Black Dog', Depressions and Other Mood Swings, and How to Tame Them • Who's in Charge?

No sooner have you arrived in the arms of the midwife than, even as a newborn baby, your mind starts working overtime. You try to make sense of the bizarre and uncertain shapes, sounds and smells around you. That is what your mind is for – to protect you and enable you to survive in an indifferent if not inhospitable environment. Is the present situation OK? What's next?   Will I find it painful, or is there a reasonable chance that it will be pleasant?   The mind is incessantly reviewing these pressing questions – Homo sapiens's key equipment for survival is to test things out in the mind, before hazarding uncertainties with the body. And this starts at birth, if not before.

Our long childhood development teaches us many things. In our more rural days, we learnt that nettles sting, thistles prick and wasps, bees and especially hornets have an even nastier

sting. In an urban setting, the hazards are perhaps greater –
don't play on busy road, cars maim and kill.

We learn this emotional tagging of the everyday things in our
surroundings from those we are closest to and who have had
most to do with our earliest development. Clearly, since we
are all born into a state of advanced quadriplegia and can
move neither limb nor sphincter in any sensible fashion – our
survival depends 100 per cent on the care and nurturing we
receive during the first days, months and years of life. Much,
if not most of what we learn during these early times is valid
and reliable for the rest of our days. Some, however, is not.

Virtually everything we learn at this time is picked up
inadvertently. Initially we tend to be preoccupied with more
pressing matters – are we going to be fed? Kept warm? Or
dumped?   It is usually a safe bet to rely on our parent's
anxieties – if they are worried by busy traffic, we tend to
share their disquiet. What upsets them, must willy-nilly upset
us – to do otherwise is scarcely feasible at that age.

But, as we know too well from our own personal experience,
not all our worries are rational or soundly based. If Mum
suffers irrational tantrums (as Sam's did earlier), or Dad
becomes unduly roused (as we saw happened to Freud), we
cannot at this tender early age tell the difference.

Only later, when things begin to go wrong, does the
possibility arise that our parents could have been, if not
wrong, then ill-advised. But for some there is not time
enough for this to happen, ever. There are those for whom
the parent–child bond has been drawn so heavily that even to
consider this as a possibility is too much. This was certainly
true for Freud – and if a man of such enormous mental talent
and capabilities could not review his own formative
influences, then doing so is clearly not an easy task, however
simple it may sound in principle.

The Invisible Roadblock

So, as you move forwards to the next stage in life, you may find an impenetrable hazard blocking your healthy progress. You cannot see it or evaluate it – you merely suffer its consequences. It seems as valid as not running across busy roads. Your pathway forwards has imperceptibly become labelled highly dangerous and absolutely impassable.

You cannot see the danger, but you presume without further examination that there is a landmine ahead. You cannot see it, because of course it is designed to be well hidden – and designed, moreover, by someone who knows best how to hide things from you – you. Your own mind blocks you – and this blockage goes so deep into what you have always learnt and know for a certainty to be true, that it takes something out of the ordinary to shift it. But shift it you assuredly can – what else is Emotional Health about?

Looking at this from another angle – how can it be sensible or rational to manufacture and distribute real landmines? These are not intended to reduce the risk to the rest of us from some natural threat – their sole function is to maim or eliminate other members of our own species. The human mind should be discerning perils in the real world, not increasing them.

Just as the landmine is very effective at blowing legs off passers-by, especially children – and it does this for decades after it was originally planted – so in the mind, the effect, and indeed the origin, is remarkably similar. An irrational and ill-considered fear leads to 'no-go' areas being created, which in both cases take unusual courage to circumvent.

The most striking image we associate with landmines today is that of Princess Di, wearing an unfashionable apron to cover her main body parts and a distinctly non-Ascot hat to protect her face. Thus attired, she walks towards known minefields. The people accompanying her look worried. As indeed they should. Landmines are exceptionally effective at blowing off heads or limbs, from which no amount of portable gear can offer any serious protection.

So why did Princess Di do this?   And why were so many delighted that she did?   Viewed from the axiom we considered in Part One, her bravery in confronting explosive damage, whether flesh and blood or political, serves to reinforce the view that all humanity is essentially Lovable, Sociable and Non-violent, and this is a goal we all aim for. Her courage reinforces our own.

For mental landmines are just as invisible and just as certain to cause serious damage, if not death, should they be inadvertently touched upon. However innocent the feelers that are put in their direction, the threat of damage is there, as it was with Sam earlier. With real landmines, it is the area around the device that is feared as much as the explosive itself. With mental landmines, of course, the really devastating effect happens well before the explosion – namely thought paralysis, or mental blindness, which for a thinking species is crippling indeed.

Only by constructing situations in which mental landmines are available for rethinking can their sinister and otherwise permanent poison be drawn. These conditions may be difficult to procure, and are quite impossible without abundant supplies of Truth, Trust and Consent.

There is nothing more deeply embedded in the infant's mind than the fact that your parents are your life-support system. For infants there is simply no substitute. If the choice is between warmth and being dumped on a freezing mountainside, or between delicious, nurturing food and certain starvation, this is not a difficult decision for the human mind to make, however young.

The irony is that the less stable the parent–child link, the more the child clings tighter. Harlow was a biologist whose experiments with monkey infants in the 1950s showed that baby monkeys threw themselves at substitute mothers even when the latter were covered in barbed wire, and drew blood every time they came for a cuddle. We humans are no different. We reason that by working harder or performing better, we can somehow improve our parental resources and supplies. The reality is that the human infant is 100 per cent dependent – only later in life do we become interdependent, and by then these deep-seated fears and insecurities may be so far down as to be virtually beyond reach. They were for Freud.

If as a dependent child, our parent holds uncongenial political views, like sexism or racism – these characteristics are heavily overshadowed by everyday questions of our very survival. The mind is there to ensure survival and if that means adopting extreme views, how is the pre-verbal infant to know any better?

When you are young, your parents are in charge – without their Consent, support and approval your life expectancy is zero. I developed an image to convey this graphically. Imagine you are suspended 50 metres over jagged rocks between a giant finger and thumb – you will say or do anything to the owner of these digits to dissuade them from dropping you.

Parental injunctions carry weight. But, for all that, parental coercion is of limited duration – when you are bigger than they, or live longer, their views, their axioms, carry significantly less weight. Unless, of course, you insist on repeating their errors and irrationalities till the cows cease coming home.

The human mind is infinitely flexible. To accommodate a perceived parental injunction, it will tie itself in more knots than you could imagine. Not only does it stop you doing what you want, but it can have you leaping through hoops of almost unimaginable nonsense. I have had customers who insist on becoming men even though they were born women, and vice versa. One even thought he would have to become a woman because only in that way could he escape his parental injunction to be violent. Again the only sensible escape route is via the aphorism *'parenting keeps infants alive, but adults insane'.* This is a message that the grown-up infant may have difficulty in hearing – it requires quantities of Truth, Trust and Consent. It also requires substantial courage and encouragement to approach these apparently lethal landmines.

Several of my customers have described parental injunctions which go way beyond the norm. They decline, as did Freud, to hear any demur on their parents' behaviour. But, worse, they are labouring under the parental injunction to end all parental injunctions: 'Thou Shalt Not ... Be.' This took me a long time to acknowledge. The person sitting in front of me, living and breathing much as I was, nevertheless insisted that their very existence depended on a ghostly parental precept – their very being hanging on an unreliable parental thread. Not an easy thing either to describe or to witness. From this sort of twisted irrationality comes suicide.

 The aim of Emotional Health is first to recognize and then to reverse the infantile pattern, to move from dependent infantile emotional survival strategies to those more appropriate for an interdependent adult, in which your intentions, social skills and support networks are up to you, not up to 'them'. From this it follows that the real parental obligation, as later chapters explore, is twofold – bring the child up and bring the child up to be independent. As your self-confidence, autonomy and empowerment grows, so too does your Emotional Health.

Opening the Box and Tidying Your Mind

Irrational emotions are most irritating because there's no point to them. They make no sense. They arise, thrash around, inflict mayhem, without explanation or reason. The victim of them cannot make sense of them – they distinctly do not wish to know. For some emotional storms, of course, the causes are all too obvious – superwomen and supermen we are not – above a certain threshold we all crack. But we break most painfully when the more potent cause of our stress is hidden from us, by us.

To counter this emotional blindness, one essential rule of Emotional Health is that there always is a cause for these irrational emotions. It may not be obvious – but where emotions erupt there is always a cause, an originating context. Indeed the only remedy for any emotional storm, aberrant or otherwise, is to find out the reality behind it – and fix it.

So if you come across a free-floating fear, the first thing to decide is that it has an anchor. It may seem to be floating free of all logical or realistic connection. Indeed its owner is likely to go to some lengths to maintain this notion of unconnectedness. But the Truth is, emotions always come from somewhere. The term 'free-floating' is a misnomer, a nonsense.

So here is a challenge. Truth, Trust and Consent determine that the individual with the aberrant emotion needs to give their Consent for it to be examined. Yet it is immediately apparent that this is the last thing they wish to think through. Left to their own devices, as with Sam earlier, there is no way they will bring themselves to think clearly about the origins of their own irrational emotional storms.

After 25 years moving ever nearer the critical point, I stumbled upon the root of the problem. One way to illustrate it is to describe it as a box. As the child grows up, exploring the world around, something dreadful happens. They suffer severe abuse, for example, or a parent dies. From this the child learns that this world is not a safe place; it holds unaccountable dangers. The child does the only thing he or she can – they withdraw. 'This is not happening to me.' The child has no other recourse. All human children are small, dependent and socially incompetent – they cannot fend for themselves until older. So if something happens which appears to them to threaten their life, they do the only thing they can – they deny it. They shut it away in a box, with walls and lid as thick as they can manage.

The cleverer they are and the more mental resources they have – then the more successful they are in hiding the dreadful item away. The child's remedy is to put as much mental furniture between the terror and themselves as they possibly can. Later they fend off all intrusions, incursions or enquiries into what might be in the box with as much vigour as they would any other threat to their very lives, their very existence – whence the intensity of irrational emotions.

If they are very clever, powerful, highly articulate, with a multitude of talents, they can keep their box untouched until they are well over 80 – Freud did.

The sovereign remedy for all such boxes is Truth. For the astonishing thing about this box is that it is now empty. What was true in infancy is false in adulthood. Adults differ from infants. Infants cannot arrange their next meal – adults can run an entire career. All infants are surrounded by adults two or three times their size, their strength and capabilities, who are more or less trustworthy. Adults are, or should be, a great deal more self-sufficient.

But we need to bear in mind where this box came from. It is empty now – but it certainly wasn't. Its constructor closed it for a powerful, primitive reason – they wished to survive. When you ask where these irrational emotions come from, you are in effect inviting that individual to put their head above the parapet to scan the wider horizon – and, in their terms, to guarantee their own immolation.

Freud did not know what his irascible father might do next. He heard the scorn in his father's voice – his father thereby became an unreliable life support. Freud knew very well, as do all seven-year-olds, that survival depends on parental goodwill – for some reason quite unknown to him, he had lost his father's favour. Freud feared that the consequence would be terminal. Infanticide does occur. Children are left on doorsteps. How was Freud to know that such a fate did not await him – 'next'?

The only remedy for such a pressing infantile dilemma is reliable parental support, an adequate supply of Truth, Trust and Consent from the large powerful adults around. Yet this is precisely what is in jeopardy. Freud could not avoid noticing that his father was expressing 'distancing' emotions from him. His father was not endearing himself to his son. No, his father, for reasons of his own irrationality, was stoutly declaring that the boy had no future. To a child this is decidedly akin to a death sentence. It was one which Freud was unable to address in the next 73 years – no one came close enough, was trusted enough, to invite Sigmund to open the lid.

So what would it have taken to persuade the adult Sigmund to look inside the box? First of all, you would need to know that all threatened infants do this – they construct mental boxes for their own survival. Next you would have to know that the box is now empty and that the defences need redirecting. And finally it needs enough Truth, Trust and Consent, and to spare.

These are difficult things to arrange. It is not always possible to express the invitation to open the box, in sufficiently attractive terms – but this is the central challenge of Emotional Health. Emotions are busy saving lives – that is their ineradicable job. The fact that they are running on lines which have not changed since infancy is difficult to correct. But at least this is a blueprint which makes sense.

The intriguing feature of irrational emotions is that the mind in which they are occurring, and which seems to others to be suffering most from them, has resolved, with fanatical determination, not to do anything about them. So you find drug addicts insisting they are living in Seventh Heaven, when, to outsiders, their lives are obviously in ruins. You find anorexics determined to achieve ridiculously low body weights, inducing weakness and physical handicaps which others would find quite intolerable. Yet these afflicted individuals maintain they are 'happy' with the status quo. No wonder my first psychiatric tutors resigned themselves to the notion of 'hopeless neurotics'.

But it is entirely wrong to suppose that, because the client can see no way out, that therefore there is none, that they are in fact 'untreatable'. And the first thing to remedy here is to reinstate the notion of intent. There is no way any of us can achieve mental stability, let alone root out irrational and destructive emotions, unless we are credited with the ability to have intentions. We are not mindless, unfeeling robots and we do not deserve to be treated as such, however 'scientific' such treatment may be.

Whatever intent is, it is safer and healthier to assume that we have it, rather than that we don't. Without the ability to move our mental furniture about as we wish, which only intent can give us, we would be left with a permanently chaotic mind. Intent may be impossible to define, even to think very clearly about – but it's there, and I encourage every one of my customers to exert their own, to the fullest degree that they can. This, by any other name, is autonomy.

This is essentially what good parents do. In bringing the child up, and in bringing him or her up to be independent, the child is gently encouraged to assert control over increasing aspects of his or her life. Responsibilities, decisions and other tasks are gradually devolved from capable parental shoulders to the young, risky and initially totally incapable shoulders of the infant. Not an easy progression – but vital.

Parents have responsibilities which they may or may not fulfil – but the last thing we should do, contrary to Freud's explicit advice, is seek to be substitute parents. A radically different approach is called for. Our task today is to encourage those who operate infantile survival strategies to acknowledge the Truth that they are adults. They will tend to disagree. Their primitive emotional drives are set towards securing stable parents – since this is what they desperately needed in infancy. In adulthood, what they now desperately need is encouragement to stand on their own two feet. They need to improve their social skills, their self-esteem and their access to reliable supplies of Truth, Trust and Consent, so that they can unblock their frozen fears and become ever Emotionally Fitter.

'Black Dog', Depressions and Other Mood Swings, and How to Tame Them

Suppose you have a problem to solve – you set to work, put your mind to it and expect to make progress. If you meet problems you redouble your efforts, try alternatives and press on. After a while, if there is still no progress, you might begin to wonder if it was worth the candle. However, if the problem is pressing and the solution to it vital, this extra pressure begins to weigh you down. If you still find progress slow or non-existent, a degree of disheartenment is bound to creep in, which can slowly descend into despair.

Emotions are life-saving, so they press you in a direction which seems on the surface to be safer (or it did). But suppose these emotions were blind. How would they know a safe route from disaster? Nag, nag, nag, push, push, push – the pressure builds, the way forward is unclear to the point of being invisible – so something has to give. They push you in one direction, which, if you cannot think it through, may be quite impossible. The commonest, as discussed in a later chapter, is being simultaneously both a son and a husband, or a daughter and a wife. Often these roles rub happily along together, but where they do not they may be quite impossible to reconcile – whence one source of despair. We are none of us superman or superwoman – we have our thresholds, and when stress builds too high, we crack, whoever we are.

Now the curious thing about emotions is that, though the cause of irrationality is always the same – 'frozen terror' – the manifestations vary across an infinite range. Indeed it is this variability which has quite flummoxed the medical profession. Whereas you can classify tuberculosis, for example, by the type of organ it infects – emotions are so fluid and shapeless that the diseases they inflict are never two the same.

Every person is different from every other – there may be similarities, but there are never identicalities. Precisely the same holds true when these individuals are afflicted by a mental disease, schizophrenia say, or depression. Every such individual has depression or psychosis in their own unique way. Classifying psychiatric conditions by attempting to tie mental disorders down to ever smaller pigeonholes is akin to describing each wave on the beach – next time you look, they have all changed.

This calls for another of those invaluable scales or spectrums. Place the milder diseases at one end and the more severe at the other – and watch how the same individual can waltz through all of them, even on the same afternoon. At one end are the neuroses – nowadays going under the alias 'Personality disorder', at the other the psychoses – whether schizophrenia, manic depression or otherwise.

As with the emotions, such a scale is not watertight – it leaks. In this, it faithfully reflects its subject matter – there is nothing so variable and so unconstrained as the human mind, especially when disordered. But some mental disorders are manifestly more serious than others. Thus psychoses appear to break contact with reality, if only for a while, whereas neuroses merely insist on trying to distort it.

As with emotions, it helps to catch each symptom as it flits or half-flits past you, and to allocate it to one of two groups – mild or severe, neurotic or psychotic. This is more helpful than pinning out variants, like so many insects on a cork board. And all the while, under every aberration, there is a hidden fear, a camouflaged box, an unseeable landmine. However colourful or exotic the symptomatology, unless this dangerous item is addressed and detoxified, the disease cannot be said to be cured.

As for depressions, their origin is not really so mysterious. Anyone who hits upon an insoluble problem which **must** nevertheless be solved – once the limit is reached, despair beckons, especially when you cannot be persuaded to see the true irrational cause.

Winston Churchill, a man of more resources than most, was afflicted episodically by what he called his 'black dog' – he suffered from bouts of depression. This was not the best feature of a wartime leader to advertise widely, since its widespread dissemination might tend to undermine morale. It goes to show that, however capable you are in other respects, if there are childhood landmines or 'frozen terrors' within, then whatever your outward strengths, you remain vulnerable to invisible problems and afflictions from inside – until you can grow up emotionally.

On the other hand, if the cause of the disease can be found and rooted out, then, as in all other medical contexts, the malady can be declared cured. This applies to the psychoses as much as to any other disease.

Just as the human mind is the most remarkable item in the entire cosmos, so the range of its symptoms when it 'fails' or becomes disordered, is infinite – a fact that should not in the least surprise us. Perhaps the most remarkable is the effect this disruption has on mood. Just as emotions 'move' thoughts about, as described in Part One, so too they set the scene for all other mental machinations. Mood is something to do with the background, the backdrop against which the drama, if any, unfolds.

So when the emotions are at loggerheads, either with each other, or with external reality, they can set up the wrong scenery entirely. Perhaps the most dramatic is the manic condition, in which whole battalions of emotions surge up from below and quite swamp what you were otherwise thinking of doing.

When I walked on to my first psychiatric ward, in 1963, I was somewhat taken aback to be accosted by a young man, about my age, who made great play on the similarity of my name with that of the illustrious Dr Samuel Johnson. He did not strike me as dangerous, merely insistent on pursuing one line of argument to the exclusion of all else. And this, of course, is the clue that we have come to look for. What is it that the pressure of thoughts or emotions diverts our attention from?

This is precisely the problem described earlier – the individual is desperately throwing all his or her mental furniture in the way, so as not to have to think about a deep-seated mental agony. To dismantle this 'defence' we need quantities of Truth, Trust and Consent. And as with all these well-hidden, thick-walled boxes, it is not we who open the lid, it is the owner of the box who does, or does not, as the case may be. But until she or he does, the surges will continue, since the job they have set out to do (however misconceived or ill-timed) remains unfinished.

Because the afflicted individual cannot see where these emotional surges come from, their very power can take him or her unawares. The surges can come at any time, and they sweep away all other considerations. The last customer I treated for this condition, also a young woman of 20, would croon loudly in the corner of the ward, ostensibly oblivious of the effect this tuneless harassment had on others. The rest of the ward came to dread these noisy interludes. After a time, she conceded that she rather enjoyed being swept along, while at the same time fretting that she had lost control. The two aspects were delicately balanced. I encouraged her to favour the second, get her feet more firmly on the ground and cut the roots of the buried emotions so she could be yet again, in control.

In her case that emotion was anger. She was adamant that she did not need to be angry. Anger for her did not exist. She had in fact been grossly abused previously – but her training was such that she had been deprived of all means of expressing any anger, even of irritation at such injustices. Partly therefore her manic moods were a means of avoiding the issue of what to do with her 'trapped anger', to which she was initially totally blind. And partly they were a splendidly colourful diversion from the whole painful topic. Either way, the box remained closed, Emotional Health remained out of reach and the landmine retained its awesome lethal potential.

Moods can seriously interfere with your mental harmony. You can be chirruping happily along, when something quite trivial happens, or occurs to you, and you sink slap bang into the mire. All such unregulated emotions, whether pushing or changing the scenery, come from the same source. Emotions are always trying to save your life. If they are urging you in the wrong, or irrational, direction – there is only one explanation – they have got stuck in a time-warp and are loudly advising that the best thing for you would be a really comfortable nursery or a sumptuous kindergarten.

It's that box again. However desperate you may be to make its walls as thick and impenetrable as you can – it leaks. Part of you knows, just as Sam did, that all is not quite as it should be. But most of you doesn't want to know. So all the while, the potential for serious pollution of the remainder of your mental circumstances continues to hang over you.

Who's in Charge?

It is really a question of confidence. Who's in charge?   Is it you, with your schemes for making ends meet?   Or is it some monstrous time bomb from earlier years, seething and spluttering away in the depths, hazarding what you hold most dear?   These seething, surging emotions are now out of date. They may be pressing you to improve your parental circumstances – but they need to learn that, though parenting keeps infants alive, it keeps adults insane. As before, the switch to turn these obsolete emotions off is entirely in the hands of the victim him or herself. Persuasion, not coercion, is the name of the game.

The key is to provide enough supplies of Truth, Trust and Consent, to enable the afflicted individual to re-evaluate what was painfully true a long time ago but is no longer. For unless and until sufficient resources and support can be ferried in, the box lid will remain tightly shut. If it does not, the victim believes there's no tomorrow.

The role that intent plays in this battle is highly significant. Where there are no-go areas, there will always be a risk that the box will burst and flood the scene with all sorts of hot, strong and totally misplaced emotions. Psychiatrists today are taught that intent is illusory. Nevertheless, unless we can encourage and guide the victim's intentions into calmer, more mature, more adult waters, mental stability is at risk and Emotional Health ever more distant.

Conversely, by embracing the notion that the individual is, or is quite capable of being, fully in charge of all their mental furniture, especially the aberrant items – here is an optimistic blueprint waiting to be implemented. And, being Sociable animals, the Fitter others are Emotionally, the more secure are we all.

5 Violence – Where It Comes from and How to Cure It

Tantrums • Curing the Disease of Violence • Road-rage, Trolley-, Parking-and All the Other '-rages' • Judicial Ignorance of Child Abuse • Vengeance, Punishment and Retribution Are All Irrational • Curing Tantrums

The Korean shopkeeper stood beside his burnt-out premises after the Los Angeles riots, mourning several of his friends who had just been shot and bewailing a well-known film star for his misinformation about living with guns. 'In the movies,' he said, 'it's always the bad guys who are killed – in real life, it's the good.' This is the key to the downside of the Hollywood Syndrome.

Emotions, as we have seen, label otherwise neutral items with value – good or bad. They also sell. The stronger emotions sell more heavily than the milder or friendlier ones. Thus blood and gore have been a staple since earliest times. The Roman Coliseum demonstrated an unhealthy escalation – from one murder to several, from one rape to several, from human rape to animal rape and so on, much as our visual 'entertainment' does today.

Emotions are there to alert and guide us through problems. We learn to pay attention to them, it pays to do so. But we are an imitative species – what we see, we copy. This is generally an excellent social device, though it can have serious drawbacks. Advertising sells. If you hear repeated often enough that 'Bloggs is Best', this may surreptitiously induce in your mind, especially in the background, or backdrop, the notion that Bloggs is better than Cloggs, or some such. This is unreasoned, unthought through.

Television and the other visual media advertise violence. All the guys in the black hats are shot dead before the end of the movie. Can it be entirely coincidental that the death penalty has recently spread across the majority of states in the USA. There is clear medical evidence that watching violence encourages violent behaviour. The commercial pressures in favour of exhibiting violence represent a serious source of anti-social acts. Small wonder that the Non-violent part of the second basic axiom faces an uphill struggle.

The evidence in favour of the assumption that we are all born Non-violent is strongest where you would least expect it – among the most violent men in the British prison system. There you find a rather different reality. During my five years in Parkhurst Prison I worked in a Special Unit for the most violent, unstable, ill-disciplined lifers. Referrals were made from prisons all over England. Indeed it had been established to cater for troublemakers, especially those too violent for Broadmoor. From my work with them, it became obvious that violence is a disease, a learned disease. If you give them a chance, they prefer to be Non-violent.

These most violent prisoners were not born violent. They had been brought up to violence. They were surprised when I invited them to take an alternative viewpoint. After a couple of years they much preferred this alternative – so much so that when the Prisons Inspector came round, they proudly informed him that no alarm bells had been rung for two years – a world record in any maximum-security prison wing. This is a counter-cultural message – many, especially Michael Howard, the Home Secretary of the day, preferred to believe that violent men are born evil. He applied to the High Court to prevent this alternative viewpoint being shown in a BBC Panorama documentary on my work in March 1997. Happily, the judge took a more civilized view.

It was while working with these men that it became inescapable to me that we are all born Lovable, Sociable and Non-violent. It was there that the values of Truth, Trust and Consent showed through, and proved their mettle. The conventional wisdom, backed by today's media, endorses the reverse – violence emotes, and what emotes sells.

The impact of the flood of visual images on our wider social structures that so characterizes our present era is hard to underestimate. Where Homer had mere words and Shakespeare strutting players, we have special effects upon special effects – none of which need touch down on reality at any stage, to our cost. It has been estimated that a child in today's culture will have seen 10,000 homicides on TV before he or she is 11 years old. There is a close parallel with nicotine – today it is no longer socially acceptable to smoke. In a few years' time, should a more rational ethos prevail, it will be just as socially unacceptable to present wanton violence in a favourable light.

I do not advocate compulsory censorship of visual material. It's just that Emotional Health entails that we all recognize that we are social animals. Therefore the more Sociable we can make ourselves, the more stable our minds, and indeed our societies, will become. From this it follows that we do not need to be coerced into behaving in a socially responsible manner, rather than otherwise. Vacuous portrayal of violence is socially irresponsible and in due course will be seen as such.

Tantrums

Violence is infantile. That goes for all violence – every violent act is essentially what you would expect from a child – and explicitly not from a mature adult. As a serial killer in the making put it to me – if a four year old has a tantrum, he stamps his foot – whereas a tantrum in a 24-year-old can lead to murder. It is a difference in size and strength. Though, of course, any two-year-old can pull a feather-light trigger and immolate anyone within range.

Violence is invariably irrational. It follows that it is invariably counterproductive. It produces an apparent short-term gain. But since we humans respond worst to fear – and violence is intended to be fearsome – it erodes rather than cements our social support networks. Violence is therefore anti-social, and if we are to repair our social cohesion it needs to be seen as pathological. Steps need to be taken to educate us all, especially the young and the media moguls, that a Non-violent, Sociable community is better able to promote 'Lovability' all round.

Given that violence is invariably irrational, it follows that its victims, especially of the 60 or so murderers I got to know in Parkhurst, were only coincidentally part of the picture. It became apparent that the victim was someone who happened to be in the wrong place at the wrong time. The real target of the violence, as with the origin of all irrational emotions, was someone else, from some other era. In the case of these 60, the person they murdered had inadvertently stepped into the shoes of a figment of the murderer's imagination, generally a parental figment. Indeed in one case, the prisoner actually said he saw a flashback of his father's face on the man he was about to stab. After he killed him, he had five minutes' grace, during which time he was relieved to think that his father would never again be able to sexually abuse him. Reality came tumbling back and his 'frozen terrors' regained their former potency. These are the lethal consequences of the dreaded box described earlier.

60

Never once was this pattern used by my customers as an excuse – 'I held the knife or the gun – I killed him,' they would say. 'But it was my father in my head, behind it all.' When we started, not one of them had any sensible reason as to why they had committed their crime – they simply didn't know. Once they found out, they were invariably remorseful and showed more concern for the victim than does the current criminal justice system.

Tantrums arise through an outburst, an upsurging of rage, with or without the red mist we meet later. Clearly, as we gain emotional maturity and our degree of Emotional Health improves, all such infantile baggage fades to zero.

Curing the Disease of Violence

Working with the most violent prisoners provided me with a unique opportunity to find out what the roots of violence are and how they might be cut. From a position where violence was clearly a disturbing phenomenon, whose parameters were essentially unknown – it became clear to me that the individuals I was dealing with in Parkhurst did not, deep down, wish to be violent.

They were very familiar with violence, they knew it backwards. Some had been instructed by their fathers as follows: 'If he hits you, pick up a stick. If he has a stick, pick up a knife. If he has a knife, pick up a gun.' The logic of escalating your weaponry against his may be as old as pre-civilization itself, but it withers once you take the wider view. If your longer-term goal is to build up a reliable social-support network, the best way forwards is to refrain from infantile violence and childish coercion. And then to educate parents, schools and others in our wider society, in the same direction.

Indeed in this Special Unit in Parkhurst Prison, all the evidence pointed to the fact that we had eliminated violence –

it had been cured. The statistics are irrefutable – during the first seven and a half years there were 42 incidents of recorded violence – during the last two and a half there was one, a reduction of over 95 per cent. These are not my figures – they come from the official Special Unit records. The then Home Secretary disregarded them, closing the unit because he disagreed fundamentally with the principles on which it was based.

Though unpopular with the Prison Service, others were interested in my findings. Thus I found myself running a workshop in a nearby city, where curbing violence had become a priority. The title I gave my workshop was 'Curing Violence'. When the chairman read out the programme he could not swallow this, so offered to change it on the hoof. 'Let's say "Reducing Violence",' he suggested. 'No,' I interrupted, 'it sounds outrageous, but curing violence is what I mean.'

Later in the conference, after I had given my small workshop, a distinguished senior police officer leaned across the table during a pitifully small interval and purred: 'Convince me.' I was happy to oblige. I informed him first that I was not going to tell him anything he did not already know. If there was a scuffle going on in the far corner of the room, he, as an experienced policeman, would know exactly what do to. He would first establish a personal relationship with the antagonists. He would also know for a fact that there was something in the background, something slightly unreal that had contributed to the fighting – there were figments in their minds which triggered the violence. 'I engineer the removal of those figments.'

Of course, these figments arise from the 'frozen terrors', from the unseen landmines, the hidden-away boxes we have met already. But rest assured – once these infantile remnants are removed Non-violence does indeed blossom. And as it does, so Emotional Health becomes an ever more reliable reality.

Road-rage, Trolley-, Parking- and All the Other 'Rages'

'I don't know what came over me! I just lost it. A red mist seemed to come down and I went berserk.' If you listen to some of the judgements handed down in open court, in which sentencing judges describe the offender as someone who knowingly and deliberately did ghastly things, you might be taken aback to find that the offender him or herself has no real knowledge of what happened at all. 'I just went too far.' Or: 'He had it coming' – whatever that might be supposed to mean.

All sorts of horrible things are done on the spur of the moment. This is not to deny that they occur. But if you can succeed in gaining the offender's confidence, you will find a large black hole of ignorance regarding the origins of the offence.

By now we can recognize this ignorance – it pays the individual not to know. Further, by applying the rule that infantile emotions always trump adult ones, it follows that these large emotions must come from infancy. Finally, to confirm this 'diagnosis' and remedy the disease such that it does not occur again, we must supply adequate doses of Truth, Trust and Consent, under cover of which we may, just may, be able to persuade the offender to open that toxic box that hitherto they have so desperately tried to hide.

Alternatively you might be persuaded to accept the notion that these matters are fully determined, that we need to find the 'clockwork' pieces which fit, jigsaw-like, into the given context. You would then start by collecting all the different rages into their separate piles. Thus you might start with road-rage and see who is most likely to succumb. Then, in a different category, you could accumulate all the trolley-rages which occur not on the highway, but in the innocent supermarket. After this there are the parking-rages – someone slips into your cherished spot when you are already labouring under enormous pressures, so you pull out your handy 'self-protection' machine-pistol and you end their parking career for ever – believe me, it happens.

The criminal justice system, from the police to the judiciary to the prisons, may then step in, remove the offender from the scene for a period, only to release him or her back on to the streets, even more bitter than before, with no way of seeing any more clearly where the damage came from, or how possibly to control it. Current prison policy is too preoccupied with punishment, overlooking the obvious fact that brutalizing criminals increases crime.

Meanwhile the victim, the real sufferer on the scene, receives nothing – no recompense, no comforting, no support – this is the real injustice. Were I in charge, I would insist the offender meet the victim or the victim's family so that some form of restorative justice is agreed. I would confront every offender, or pre-offender, with the reality of what they had done (especially as the victim saw it), ask them where the emotions came from which underlay it, and not let them go until they could assure me and their peers that they now understood the origins of these violent upsurging emotions, and so could control them.

As with all irrational emotions, the key point is that the rage is not powered by the context which triggers it. It comes, bottled up, from an earlier era, arising from unfinished business at an earlier age. It is not the stealing of your missed parking spot that provokes the storm, but the blind rage arising from the misperceived notion that if you don't get it, you're dead. All emotions, even those that seem most barbaric, are filling some sort of role in the life-protection business. The threat to that particular offender's life is now firmly in the past. Sadly, the 'life-saving' rage, terror and tantrums associated with it have yet to join it there.

Terror and rage are infantile – their current purveyor needs to be convinced of this, by persuasion rather than coercion. They need to be persuaded that life is safer in adulthood than it ever could be in infancy. Horrendously powerful emotions are no longer needed, which is essentially what Emotional Health means. Emotional Health is within the reach of all. And that means all.

Judicial Ignorance of Child Abuse

Let's take Stan as an illustration of 'chip-shop' rage. Now Stan was not a heavyweight criminal, indeed he was a highly personable and likeable character. Moreover, he was only 17 and this was his first offence. But what he did sounded very frightening and could have led to much more damage than it did. He was apprehended following a fracas at the local chip shop, where, egged on by his mates and under the influence of alcohol, he threw a number of items around the shop and at the shop assistant. However he continually backed away from direct fist-to-fist contact, especially when the latter waved a large knife at him. From my extensive experience of violent men in Parkhurst Prison, I could see that his heart had not been in it. Nevertheless he was arrested and brought before the magistrates.

I was asked to see Stan and draw up a psychiatric report for the court as to what had happened and what his further risk was likely to be. The story that emerged was heartrending, but, sadly, it did nothing to mitigate the magistrates' judgement, nor the judge's on appeal.

Stan's childhood was a nightmare. Johnny, one of his mother's 'husbands', terrorized the whole family for a number of years. Johnny, I later discovered, had been well known to the statutory authorities – he had an unusually violent character, with a penchant for beating Stan's mother. Johnny regularly threatened the family at knifepoint, causing the family to spend extensive periods of time in women's refuges, such that Stan's schooling became badly disrupted. He said he could read, but his maths is poor, essentially because having missed crucial stages in his education, he never had a chance to catch up.

What broke Stan, however, was the fact that Johnny contrived to split up the family so thoroughly that Stan finally lost all contact with his beloved brothers and sisters – they were moved out of contact with him. When he didn't hear from them one Christmas, it broke his heart. It was then that the nightmares started. He was being chased by Johnny waving a knife at him and trying to kill him, much as had happened in reality a few years earlier. What could Stan do? The nightmares were unrelenting. Right or wrong, he began to drink heavily, trying as best he could to 'drown' these fearsome images and horrendous flashbacks.

The only thing Stan remembers of the incident in the chip shop is the knife being waved at him – it was this which, unbeknownst to the shop assistant, triggered Stan's overreaction. It was the appearance of the knife which caused Stan to 'lose his head'. It is highly significant that this is the one item which percolated intact through his alcoholic haze. Ironically, this is also the one item the alcoholic desperately wishes to 'drown', as a later chapter explores. There's no way the shop assistant could have known that waving a knife would take Stan straight back into confrontations with Johnny, confrontations which he was bound to lose. Even Stan did not know this at the time – he simply did to want to know it.

Now, being bigger, and misperceiving himself back into a confrontation with Johnny – Stan was determined to win, overlooking the fact that his assailant was not Johnny but an innocent third party. It is these highly specific but desperately hidden keys which underlie every outburst of rage. Only by taking them into account and 'defusing' them can any progress be made, in what, in other ways is a dangerous situation. This story also indicates how today's rage has only the faintest link with the real roots of the problem – Emotional Health can require hard work in unpacking what had earlier been deliberately very well hidden.

Previous attempts at 'counselling' had been defeated by Stan's terror of even thinking about the problem. Stan would not hear of it. 'I don't think about Johnny,' he said defiantly when we first began – which is exactly how every major criminal reacted when I started. Underneath, however, they all have dreadful abuse to 'hide'. By using this 'active ignorance' as my starting point I was able to cajole Stan into shouting at his image of Johnny in an empty chair. This robust yet delicate approach gently persuaded Stan that Johnny was a thing of the past. To Stan's credit, he was able to confront these terrifying memories and begin to put them behind him. His confidence and capabilities gradually returned. He began planning for a more stable future, gaining an interview at the local training college. Then his nightmares went, and with their departure the risk of his reoffending plummeted. He was surprised and indeed delighted to note that his rage against Johnny had faded. Sadly, the magistrates sent him to prison for 12 months anyway. They placed more emphasis on punishment than on prevention of further offending behaviour – a narrow-mindedness that the judge later upheld on appeal.

Clearly, we all wish hooliganism of whatever nature to be curtailed. We all need to feel safe as we go about our legitimate business. But merely punishing those who offend, shortchanges the rest of society. Stan would only change when his terror of his stepfather's abuse had been faced and eliminated. Sending him to prison, where he associates with a group of similarly socially handicapped souls, benefits no one. It only makes things worse by destroying his future, just as he is about to become a stable, mature, civilized adult. When the true roots of violence are more widely acknowledged, then perhaps we can adopt more adult strategies for curing it. This is one indication that Emotional Health has implications for the wider society – a topic explored more fully in Part Five.

Vengeance, Punishment and Retribution Are All Irrational

However well-knit a person's protective box might be, however carefully or cunningly constructed – all such constructions are prone to leak. None of them, in the nature of things, can be totally impervious – they may be buried for years, decades even, or they may seem to have disappeared entirely – but depending on the circumstance which lead to their construction in the first place, they can still blow up, sometimes in the most unexpected places.

The challenging aspect of this, is that the only person with the key to the box, is also the last person who will willingly and voluntarily open it. But that's the disease. What is needed is to find some sort of connection between the outburst today, and the disaster in infancy from which the box was meant to provide protection.

There is always a connection. There is no such thing as a rage out of the blue. It may seem that way. The perpetrator of it might prefer it – but the evidence is against. The rage comes from an earlier time, when the resources for self-preservation were much less satisfactory.

By uncovering that painful origin it is possible to blow the whole thing away, like a puff of smoke. And when that happens, other surprising elements follow. Many of the murderers in Parkhurst for example, stopped taking sleeping pills, their tranquillizer usage dropped by 95 per cent, their stomach pains eased, they started taking Open University courses – they had ceased being infantile, they had grown up.

Once they had done that, they started educating me. One had such a long and serious criminal record, even while in prison, that he was dubbed a prisoner for his natural life. He told me he had watched the parents of the victims of the Moors Murderers over the last 30 years. He had nothing to do with that appalling crime and had never met the protagonists. But he was sad to see how mothers of the dead children appearing at news conferences about it were consumed with bitterness. The damage inflicted on the children was spreading to infect future generations. Far more should have been done for the victim and the victim's families.

One Monday morning, coming wearily into work from a heavy weekend, I toiled into my office for my first appointment. This was a young man who had assured me, when I first met him, that he was born violent and that there was nothing he or I could do about it. He was a serial killer in the making, he had killed in prison already and planned to do so 'another six or seven times'. I managed to tell him at the time that I thought violence was not genetic but learnt, but I did so with some caution.

To my surprise, on this particular Monday I suddenly found myself in an advanced seminar on vengeance that would have graced the most progressive university forensic department. The man before me was railing against the way his mother had done this, that and the other. He had perfected this violence routine and he was describing what he would like to do to her. He would pull her arms and legs off, he would torture her remorselessly. She would, so he assured me, plead for him to 'finish her off'.

Gradually, as his ranting began to fade, we uncovered the underlying fear, and it became ever clearer that vengeance is a disease. It is based on an irrational fear, a fear that has passed its sell-by date and needs to be replaced by something healthier. This does not mean to say that the offender must escape taking responsibility for his or her offence – that is only as it should be. But it does mean that the notion of 'retribution' which underlies so much of Anglo-

Saxon law is far too close to vengeance for comfort. The remedy lies in restoring matters to as near the status quo as can be. But, above all, there needs to be far greater emphasis on Emotional Health all round.

Curing Tantrums

If you watch an infant having a tantrum, you may notice his or her eyes flick over to the audience, to gauge the effect. If you are directly involved, all your attention is likely to be taken up with limiting the damage and bringing the whole unpleasant episode to as swift a conclusion as possible. If you can watch from the sidelines, you may see this odd 'feedback' loop in action. All children, of whatever age, become adept at gauging their parents' reactions, their parents' limits. To go over these limits is likely to prove too much. But to go up to them is almost obligatory – you have to know where the boundaries are, so you can plot your next strategy more precisely.

This is not a restful game. But there are ways of limiting the damage, and these again, as with all emotional turmoils, involve the prolific use of Truth, Trust and Consent, not always the easiest to deploy in infancy.

When you move on to adulthood, this limiting factor disappears. There are no longer any wary parents' faces to be scanned for signs that you might have gone too far, or any indications that enough is enough and it is time to look for face-saving devices by which to climb back into the status quo. No, as my serial killer tutor observed, a tantrum in a 24-year- old is of a different order.

Essentially a tantrum is a welling up, an overflowing of emotion, mostly rage, with some fear mixed in. But when it occurs in an adult it can be a fearsome beast to behold. The red mist that comes down, obscuring the view, is obvious enough – clarity of thought is the first casualty, swiftly followed by lack of control. But the main engine is a sudden welling up of frustration, of rage for an injustice or threat from long ago that has never been addressed or remedied.

In adulthood, this outburst is uncontrolled. Gone are the parental signposts, gone too is the original threat or injustice which the rage was called up to protect against. So the tantrum-purveyor is on their own. There is nothing to stop them any longer. They blurt out torrents of emotion in a volcano of rage. If the ethos they currently inhabit encourages violence, that will add grist to the mill. If they are denied the outward expression of anger, their violence may well be turned inwards against themselves, either through self-starvation or other methods of self-harm, including suicide.

My experience taught me that the bigger the tantrum, the more monstrous is the rage and terror which underlie it. It may be well camouflaged, but it is there all right. Patience and support will in due course be rewarded with unlocking this primitive injury.

This process of exploring deep and painful mental wounds can take years in recalcitrant cases. One man in Parkhurst Prison who had killed a number of times while in prison refused to do more than pass the time of day with me. He walked round me for nine months. 'Good morning.' 'Good morning.' 'Are you coming to see me today?' 'No chance.'

He was watching my reactions, gauging my temper. He was quick to see if I got upset when people cancelled their appointments with me. He wanted to know if, when I said Consent, I really meant it. Then abruptly, he agreed to sit down with me. We spent a gruelling six months uncovering appalling events from his childhood. He will never kill again.

Once the axiom of Lovable, Sociable and Non-violence is accepted, it is only a matter of time before the tantrummer sees that life is safer as an adult. Truth, Trust and Consent can then be seen to provide a far more reliable and secure support network than any amount of hidden boxes. For a while, it may be touch and go. But whatever the level of the problem, Emotional Health is available to all – and every rage and terror from childhood can be totally excised 100 per cent.

6 Jealousies, Guilts and Panic Attacks and How to Cure Them

Too Many Siblings • Yesterday's Defeats • Where Pangs of Guilt Arise and Making Restorations • Being Naughty • Panics, Phobias and Their Cure

Jealousy is a major irrational emotion. Its roots therefore lie in life-or-death struggles from long ago. Envy can generate a green fog every bit as destructive as the red mist just discussed.

 As an idealistic young doctor, I moved from the pill-bound psychiatry of my early medical days into the realms of family medicine or general practice. I was fascinated by how family structures impacted on mental disease. I was moved by towering ambitions to uncover a pathway through the apparently hopeless mess which contemporary psychiatry had bequeathed me – my intention was nothing less than finding the cure for mental illness. I joined a three-man general medical practice in 1967, aged 30.

The work was hard, but challenging, and I learnt an enormous amount. Before long, however, it emerged that all was not well at headquarters. One of my partners went out of his way to be rude – he denigrated my work, doubted I worked hard enough and generally undermined my position. As he did so, he explained that such expletives would, of course, be fully understandable and therefore, by implication, be excused by one familiar with the psychological need to express oneself. He little knew that the key concept I had in my knapsack at that time was a pragmatic basis for responsibility, so his offensive remarks were seen for what they were.

But where did this bizarre behaviour come from?   Why berate and attempt to do down an energetic colleague who had come into a difficult situation and was labouring hard to ease the pressures of an overworked general practice?   What could he gain by my fall?

I did my full duty, saw more patients than he did. Being younger, I could carry a heavier workload. What had I done to merit this hostility?   The more patients I saw, the harsher he became – surely it should have been the other way about. Why did he not relax, knowing I did more so he need do less?   Now, of course, I can see where these misplaced emotions came from. His view of reality had been coloured by a misperceived image from his past, into whose shoes I had inadvertently slipped. I thought at the time it might have been something to do with 'sibling rivalry', though I was not sure what that was.

Now I would resolve the riddle by putting jealousy into the spectrum with all the other emotions. It may not fit very well, but it is down at the negative end and consists of two basic elements, fear and anger. The proportion of each is not easy to pin down, indeed it may vary from case to case, since there is nothing more fluid than an emotion in action.

Too Many Siblings

But the way to control jealousy, or any of the other negative emotions, is to concentrate on the role that the master emotion, fear, plays within it. Thus, in the nursery, if one of your siblings gets a better crack of the whip, your chances of survival are reduced, or they certainly would be, if there was not sufficient to go around. This will elicit fear, which is the chief life-saving emotion. If your sibling displaces you (even partially) from the fount of all security – parental attention and support – your fear and insecurity is likely to increase.

Because parents are difficult to confront or criticize directly at that age, all your negative emotions are aimed at the safer option – namely your peers. So jealousy is sibling-bound. In adult life, maturer options should be more plentiful. Often, however, they are not, and then you may feel afflicted by too many siblings, or sibling-figures, which can be just as unsettling as it was when you were in kindergarten.

In my clinical practice I have rarely had the emotion of jealousy to deal with, on its own. It is perhaps one of the milder pathological, or irrational emotions. Nevertheless it does take its toll. Even though it might not completely paralyse your capabilities, it can very effectively sour your immediate relationships, whether in your close family or in your work.

As with all irrational emotions, the principal remedy is the Truth or reality of the situation. Truth, as we saw earlier, can never be absolute, but is vitally important nonetheless. Thus the more accurately your view, and that of your 'rivals', reflects what is actually going on – the less biting, and the less damaging will be any envy that might otherwise seep out. If you can talk things through and find channels to communicate these 'blind' emotions, they will evaporate. This is easier said than done – in my first general-practice job I was unable to achieve such a healthy catharsis. My supplies of self-confidence at that time were nowhere near enough to initiate anything of this sort. I was left to cut my losses, as best I could. But ideally, by ventilating these bitter and irrational emotions, they can be defeated.

What I would have liked to have done is sit the two partners down, go through a list of practical problems and clarify the whole issue. Perhaps a local official could have facilitated it. But it would have had to be someone we all three trusted and whose advice we were all prepared to listen to, at least.

The key to resolving such problems is to take a step back from the ongoing situation. Look at it through half-closed eyes. See if you can see the infantilism peeking through. Imagine there is a Big Daddy, whether that is the President, the Chairman of the Board, or a Big Mommy, whether the Regional Bigwig or what not – and imagine them dispensing ice creams, or cream buns or some other goodie that might elicit the infantile sibling pressures that are surfacing.

You are likely to find that there are several 'hidden agendas' going on simultaneously. All those 'boxes', each defending their own. The trick is to highlight the common purpose of the organization – whether family harmony or work productivity. The key component, as with all irrational emotions, is providing adequate supplies of Truth, Trust and Consent. Without it, deep seated fears from long ago will remain just that. With it, anything is possible.

Yesterday's Defeats

The worst-case scenario is where the person who is triggering your jealousy touches on an especially sore spot. Perhaps it was when you were pipped at the post in your younger, more incompetent days. Perhaps it threatens to bring to mind an especially humiliating circumstance where you were thoroughly mauled before a jeering crowd. We saw such an incident in the opening chapter. You were singing your heart out, in good faith, and received only jeers for comfort. You still feel slighted – and Muggins over there overlaps sufficiently in your vague memories to rekindle all the pain and fear that went with it.

This, of course, is doubly sad. For though memories of our childhood days are imprinted in our mind – today is radically different from yesterday. You were dependent then, but are an adult now, and vastly more capable. It would be a great help to you to place yesterday's humiliation in its correct time context – that is, long ago. It serves no purpose having it reaped up, and repeated upon you every time you meet a certain individual or find yourself in an echo of that earlier painful scene. The pain is being doubled and given a far longer life than it deserves – it should have been dropped and have floated off long ago.

Adulthood is vastly more capable and vastly more secure than infancy ever can be – at least it should be if Emotional Health has anything to do with it. If you are beset by jealousy or envy, seek out reliable sources of Truth, Trust and Consent, deploy these as fully as you can and rest assured that the teeth of any infantile or sibling-type jealousy will be drawn. Facilitating the delivery of these axiomatic values requires someone that all parties Trust – something that is not always reliably available, as it certainly wasn't when I started out as a general practitioner. For the underlying Truth is that, despite all our apparent differences, we really are a Sociable species and perform better when cooperating. And by helping each other unreservedly we can afford each other peace of mind and stability of social contacts in a way that is quite impossible on our own.

The irony of jealousy is that it traps you as much as it does the other person. It binds you into a situation which is long past its sell-by date. As with all serious irrational emotions, jealousy is infantile. And equally, as with all such emotions, it can be hazardous attempting to inform your co-envious peers of this salient fact – they are likely to muster overwhelming forces to compel you to retract such a calumny on their manhood or womanhood. Not many react favourably to what is initially a bald invitation to grow up.

The other day, when my nonagenarian father was asked by the Community Occupational Therapist when or how often he took a bath, he responded by crisply demanding to know if she was paid to ask such rude questions. She beat a swift retreat. Similarly, explorations into the roots of irrational emotions require the full-hearted Consent of those whose emotions are being explored. Without it, you can run into serious difficulties indeed – irrational emotions, as described in Part One, are always maximum.

Equally, though it may not seem so at the time, the only people capable of being jealous or of arousing human envy are human beings. It therefore follows – since all human beings are best viewed in the light of the second axiom – that they were all born Lovable, Sociable and Non-violent. If this is obscured by the really naughty antics they get up to, bear in mind that you are an adult, even if they seem to prefer to be otherwise.

The situation becomes complicated because several competing 'survival strategies' become entangled. It comes to seem a matter of life and death that you get that bauble or that promotion. These are the same emotions that so churn up a frustrated seven-year-old when they cannot get the latest fad – for them it's indistinguishable from a life-or-death issue. Adults should show more maturity. What these infantile emotions constantly press for is for you to have a wonderfully comfortable play room, with enough toys to keep you happy indefinitely. They do not understand that as an adult, there are bigger issues at stake. Bringing them up to date is often harder than it should be.

The whole thrust of Emotional Health is that you control these slippery emotions rather than the other way around. And the key is the difference between now and the time when the targets they are still driving for were real. Adult emotional strategies are radically different from infantile ones. As an adults you are interdependent, you aim for autonomy, for self-confidence, for the capability of managing your own affairs. We need to relate socially to as many other members of our recalcitrant species as we possibly can. For by doing so, we can build a Sociable, Non-violent and supportive community, whatever our circumstances. That is what Emotional Health is all about.

Where Pangs of Guilt Arise and Making Restorations

Suppose when you were five, during a tussle with your mother, you made as if to hit a particularly precious glass bowl. It is only a gesture, a something-I-would-do-if. But you misjudge the distance, and the bowl is no more. A great wail is in order: 'Aaaaaargh.' But then what?   After the wail you could have a session of 'I didn't really mean it. Why did I do it?   I was only making a gesture. If only I wasn't quite so clumsy. If only you hadn't shouted at me . . .' and so on.

As I recall that incident from my long, long term memory, no punishment ensued. There was just a brief group sorrow, a burying of the hatchet in grieving for the lost object of beauty. We picked ourselves up, dusted ourselves down and struggled forward in anticipation of the next tribulation.

So what should have happened?   The destructive deed was done –damage and loss had been sustained – true. The guilty party was not difficult to identify – caught red-handed with the rubber gym shoe still in hand, standing over a pile of glass shards, tears streaming.

Well, there are two aspects – external and internal. Externally, society, even a micro-society such as my brother, my mother and me, must be able to protect itself and be in a position to limit damage to itself. This is the legal or social aspect of guilt – the external aspect. Who did it, what do we do about it and how can we prevent them doing it again? This is a vitally important topic, one which shines a fierce light onto the very foundations of any society, revealing its health or ill health, like a social thermometer.

But it is the internal aspect which concerns us here. Pangs of guilt wrench the soul. The wails continue. 'I shouldn't have done it.' Well, certainly a period of contrition is in order. For a five-year-old, 30 minutes is a long time. But suppose these pangs continue. Suppose they are still there after a week, a year, a decade, a century. If they are, something is manifestly wrong.

And guilt is painful. It twists the heartstrings. It twitches the main girders of the mind. Whether the deed was intentional or not matters, but less so when we are dealing with these self-inflicted pangs, which seem to take on a life of their own. And that is the clue to their resolution. Once the first wail has died down, and all avenues by which the damage might be repaired have been explored and implemented, then the guilt should fade. If it persists and becomes detached from the facts of the case, we begin to sniff an element of the irrational. Something else has entered the fray, something not altogether healthy.

As with all irrational emotions, reality is the key. So often when guilt cranks up the agony, there is a temptation to pretend, to entertain the comforting notion that perhaps it didn't really happen. There is a distinct danger that you may feel comfortable wallowing in the make-believe that it might have been different. If only . . . Those who indulge in wishful thinkings pay a heavy penalty. They are increasing the deceit and undermining the Truth, thereby sealing shut the only available escape hatch.

If guilt is so painful, what is it for?   All emotions are life-saving, so how can guilt help?   If the fire is hot, the pain of burnt fingers means that you do not lose an arm. If the mental pain of guilt is sharp enough, you feel dissuaded from repeating your mistake, or such actions as took place in the neighbourhood of your disgraceful act.

So, provided guilt is doing its job, everything is as it should be. This sounds straightforward enough, but in some instances guilt may become so painful, perhaps hitching a ride on earlier emotional tangles, that it has the opposite effect to the one intended. Far from helping cope with realities, it may make reality too painful – and then the emotions have a field day.

Underneath every guilt there is an element of fear. There is also a smidgen of anger, which hots things up, and drives the wheels faster – but the key emotion, indeed the master emotion, is fear. And, as before, the way to undo fear is to find where it comes from and lift the threat. So if you are wracked with guilt, do whatever you can to remedy the damage, and then seek out adequate supplies of Truth, Trust and Consent to unpack the underlying fear, and fix it.

In practice, how can you counter your feelings of guilt? What are the actual facts?   If you could undo what you did, what difference would it make now?   Look hard, and calculate clearly. Negotiate with the victim, the victim's family or any second party involved. Come to a compromise, restore and repair to the best of your ability. If the milk is spilt, mop it, and cooperate in replacing, or finding a replacement for it. If you insist on weeping over it regardless, have a sense of decorum, and try to resist overindulging. This is the essence of the campaign for 'restorative justice', long may it prosper. The more difficult irrational guilt requires more delicate exploration – the key is to find the mental box which we usually hide as hard as we can.

Being Naughty

There is an additional emotion which distorts matters further and sabotages even the best-laid plans. This is the label which passes under the attribute 'naughty'. It arises as follows. Parents do not have the easiest task. Their offspring are bouncing around their little world, finding where the boundaries are, testing out to see if such and such really is the limit, or can something slightly different be wangled. Do they really need to go to bed at the appointed time – how can another 15 minutes make any difference?   Many parents develop a type of emotional spray which tags certain items or acts as 'naughty' – that is, not to be entertained. So far, so good. This can be essential – if your parents do not inform you as to the risks and hazards of busy roads, who will?

But if this emotional spray of 'naughtiness' leaks, later life can be hell. The guilt which has taken on a life of its own, dips its roots into this pool of parental disapproval, sometimes long after your parents have ceased playing any part in your activities or having any wish to do so. The question then becomes: Who's in charge?   Who is responsible for your behaviour? And, as before, the spot on which your answer falls indicates how far you have progressed towards Emotional Health.

While the label 'naughty' may or may not work in infancy, it has no place in adulthood. Adults are responsible for their own acts. If they act unsociably, it's their loss. If others are deciding for you what you should or should not do, you are labouring under a handicap. What served well enough in infancy cripples later life.

We are actually whole organisms, living with whole and mysterious others in a whole society. Our peace of mind and social stability depend entirely on how we conduct our relationships, one to another. If we chose to pick out one aspect, say guilt, before moving on, we need to integrate it back into the whole. As before, the separate term 'guilt' is only for our verbal convenience.

Indeed this is part of the process of ridding yourself of guilt. Underneath every guilt, as mentioned earlier, there is a fear. The resolution of that fear cuts the hawsers anchoring the guilt, allowing it to float off into the distant yonder. Every irrational emotion has its origin in the past, an origin that is hidden in a box, the lid of which is clearly labelled 'Open this box only if you want a terminal explosion'. These labels can be potent, but all are now obsolete.

 There is another aspect of this restoration – you. Behind the label 'guilt', as indeed behind that of 'naughty', is the message that you are bad. There is something which marks you out from the crowd, something negative. Others are not like you. You are not socially acceptable. You are not good to know. If this progression is taken too far, before long you might even begin to doubt that you are Lovable.

If you are not Lovable, why bother to be Sociable? If you are not Sociable why hold out for Non-violence, against yourself or others? Plenty of scope here for childish rage and infantile tantrums. And plenty of scope too for moving steadily towards Emotional Health. For as your confidence in your own 'lovability' grows, so too will your 'sociability', the two going inexorably together. And as you become more emotionally mature, so the fangs of guilt are drawn.

Panics, Phobias and Their Cure

Imagine an earthquake taking place in your office, with filing cabinets sliding across the floor and shelves and other fixtures tumbling down. Nothing is secure, the whole world takes on a life of its own. This is how panic attacks have been described to me. Not only is everything external moving about in a totally unfixed way, but so is all your mental furniture. The worst case I had was of a woman sitting in her own kitchen, who could not cross the floor to the door or even to the next chair. Enormously powerful forces seemed to be throwing the room about, with gaping holes about to yawn beneath your feet. The floor on which you are so accustomed to stand no longer behaves as solid ground – instead the whole thing sways and threatens not only to drop you but to engulf you in an instant.

Others may be smitten while calmly sitting in their car. The fear comes over them that something dreadful is about to befall. The origin of the terror behind the attack is totally obscure, the impact utterly urgent and the outcome, though vague, horrendously dire. In fact, it is hard to think of a better illustration of 'frozen terror' than these crippling panic attacks. Raw terror is coming out to meet you.

Of course, the true roots of this terror are invisible to you, hidden away deep down inside, leaving you with the task of negotiating past the landmine you cannot even see, but whose lethal explosive consequences you know all too well.

One of my customers stretched my therapeutic capabilities to their limit. She was afflicted with severe attacks, which savagely interfered with her lifestyle. She would be walking down the street and go into a shop, then suddenly be unable to leave. Her entire surroundings would shrink and leave her no room to move. Her husband had to give up his work to look after her, because she simply could not be left.

We began locating one of her boxes, and dug it up pretty effectively. But the attacks continued. We chased another of her parental figments, twisted memories of what her parents had seemed to her as a child, which she struggled hard to bring into the present day. Still the attacks persisted.

She asked me if I had another model, other than 'frozen terror', that might help. I shrugged – I was doing the best I could, indeed the only thing I knew. She was as understanding of this as she could manage, swallowing her exasperation as best she might – but the attacks were unrelenting. She accepted that the model sounded convincing – something had happened when she was dependent on her parents for life support, but that was now a long time ago, and she now needed to be independent, especially of all parental influences. The panic attacks took no notice. She was saying all the right things, as far as I could see, but the attacks mocked us both.

She put into practice my advice of repeating that she was old enough not to need parents. She practised ordering them out of her head. The attacks failed to improve. But she stuck with the precepts. Quite how surprising this was and how courageous she was in doing so, needs emphasizing. As these terrors are being uncovered, they reveal themselves in their full horror – if supplies of security and support are delayed the hiatus can often prove so unnerving that the victim flees. She did not.

Given the lack of progress, which was unusual, I needed to think up a different angle. After much thought, I suggested she **not** think about her parent at all, that she mention him or her only when we were able to discuss it together. Here I was breaking one of my fundamental rules – the more you think in the no-go area, the better. Here I was advising her not to think in this area at all on her own, but to do so only when I was there to give active support. It took quite a wrench to come up with this one – but whoever said that human minds were straightforward.

The next thing that surprised me was that she did not take lightly my closing my clinic, which, for various reasons outside my control, I was obliged to do. She did not accept this. She rustled up some funds, and even managed to obtain funding from the Millennium Fund – and, showing considerable initiative, set about founding a 'panic attack support group'.

This group now meets regularly. I sit in on irregular occasions and discuss various management problems with her from time to time. She keeps pressing me for a video that she can show to the members of this group, so she doesn't have to repeat herself all the time (I'm working on it). Her panics are going – she can now be left for considerable periods and go shopping on her own. She finds the group she founded a help, and is sympathetic to the problems that people describe to her. This is a heartening illustration of how autonomy can indeed increase your self-empowerment.

At around this time certain conventional psychiatrists were disputing the basis of my position. So I thought I would check up on their foundations. I therefore reread the 'bible' of established psychiatry, the so-called *Diagnostic and Statistical Manual, Version Four*, or *DSM-IV*. No psychiatric patient is supposed to pass through a psychiatric facility and not acquire a coded number from one of the classifications in this weighty and bizarrely obsolete tome.

In the preamble I was horrified to read that reaction to stressful events was not regarded as a cause of mental disease. Even 'death of a loved one' was explicitly discounted as a source of mental disorders. I looked round the panic attack support group, painfully easing open those tightly clamped lids on their boxes. And three out of every four were gradually succeeding in linking their otherwise inexplicable panic attacks to the death of a parent or other 'loved one'.

These boxes were not easy to open, since the person attempting to do so was the very one who had built them in the first place. What was striking was that over 75 per cent of the group were coming to the realization that the death of their loved one had never been properly addressed. They still moved through life as if they needed parental support to survive, yet knowing at one level that their parent had died.

They knew and they didn't know. What they hadn't yet learnt was to question the belief that parental support and succour was as essential for their survival in adult life as it had been in infancy. The terrors from a failure of vital support in infancy had been transferred to open spaces, closed spaces, spiders, car doors, kitchen floors or any number of other equally irrelevant items in adult life.

If parents have difficulties in bringing up their children, and in bringing them up to be independent, it is only to be expected that the children themselves have comparable problems in their turn. Here we have a group of people who were in effect still grieving the loss of a parent. Their emotional survival strategies still entailed parental support, which, while true for every infant ever born, is the opposite of the Truth for adults.

Adults are different from infants – at least they should be. So if a parent dies when her offspring are adult, the threat to their survival is less than it would be when they were being breastfed. In the normal course of development, this is so obvious that it raises not the least remark. But when things do not run smoothly, the price to pay can be horrendous. Instead the afflicted soul struggles to fulfil what was perceived to be the parental expectation.

Even before I had disentangled the role that 'frozen terror' plays in emotional disease, I had devised a three-point plan for bereavement. The three questions I would ask my bereaved customers were – did they sometimes find themselves thinking that the deceased was still alive? Were they ever angry that he or she had left them, deserted them or dumped them? And did they sometimes believe that they could not survive without them?

What I was really probing here was the continuation into adult life of an unrealistic infantile emotional dependency which had been realistic then but was no longer. This approach must be delicate and diplomatic, since initially it may appear unduly harsh. But the Truth is that this non-supportive parental image has to be evicted from the mind if the sufferer from panic attacks or other phobias is to be relieved of their disabling symptoms.

This is not as easy as it sounds. With an adult who is moving heaven and earth to maintain a defunct parental bond, offering as a remedy precisely the opposite is quite a challenge. It is clear that an infant dies without a parent. It needs to be gently suggested that an adult might be better off without one. This may require considerable adjustment over a period of time. Nevertheless it is True that parenting keeps infants alive and adults insane. Emotional Health cannot always be acquired without a struggle.

7 Eating Disorders, Addictions and Self-harm – How to Dismantle Them

My Target Weight Is Four Stone (25 kilos) • *The Angrier I Am, the Less I Eat* • *It's Your Loss* • *Addictions – Sexaholics, Workaholics, Gamblaholics, Heroin, Cocaine and All the Other –aholics*

Those who approach adult problems armed only with infantile strategies risk finding themselves in serious difficulties. One of the most dramatic, and certainly one which most challenges conventional psychiatry, is self-harm. What can possibly possess an otherwise healthy individual to starve or otherwise injure themselves? Those who decline to give either the emotions or intent their due, find that they make no progress against such self-destructive diseases – unsurprisingly, given the circumstances.

There is an urgent need to persuade the person before you that they are adult. Until this can be achieved, anorexics and other self-harmers will drive a coach and horses through all therapeutic endeavours. The fact is that, like everyone else, anorexics have a switch within themselves, which they may or may not Consent to turn. Until you can obtain this Consent, your help is in vain.

Under other circumstances it would be laughable to see a psychiatrist struggling with wilful young girls, the one saying, 'You will eat' and the other, saying 'I won't'. It is not difficult to see misplaced parenting playing havoc here. As the saying goes, you can take a horse to water, but you cannot make it drink. Even horses are accorded the power of Consent with which those in charge of them must comply, if they wish to get anywhere at all. Why is it so difficult to apply this to anorexics?

My Target Weight Is Four Stone (25 Kilos)

The need for Consent is literally vital when dealing with eating disorders. Let me describe a young 20-year-old client, let's call her Samantha. She had a target weight of four stone (25 kilos). Where does such a ridiculous idea come from? It is neither lack of intelligence nor ignorance. The advertising industry, with its super-slim models, plays only a small part in such a severe disease, though it doesn't help. Samantha came on to my ward with a long history of self-starvation. She had just become too old for the unit she had been in recently, where she had been force-fed for long periods. Since she declined to take in food by herself, it had been deemed feasible to bypass this problem by pumping the food straight into her stomach via a naso-gastric tube. This solved one problem, the intake of calories, but, as with all coercion, its success was transient at best and highly offensive at worst.

How could Samantha 'forget' the vital importance of food? Where did this irrational decision come from? Why select four stone as her target weight? Was it not obvious to her that she would be dead long before she got there? The one thing it would be folly to do would be to doubt the strength of her self-destructive intent.

The most important advice I learned in medical school was: 'Listen to the patient, s/he is telling you the diagnosis.' In other words, listen carefully and you will hear what is wrong. Whatever you do next is therefore likely to have a better chance of success than fumbling in the dark. This aphorism even works when, as with all the other major irrational emotions, their purveyor does not want to know what the basic problem is. If you can once enlist their Trust and bounce some questions at them, even if you do not elicit a direct response, you can note which mental room they do not wish to enter – inside that room will be the mental landmine that is causing all the trouble.

In Samantha's case this advice was not easy to apply. For one thing, she spoke so softly that it was hard to hear anything, however hard you listened. For another, she was already physically weak and regularly toyed with severe electrolyte imbalance and dehydration.

To begin with, I was doing all the talking. So I plied her with the commonest question of all, one I use all the time – 'How old are you?' I asked. I was looking for 'frozen terror', I was looking for a clue to what trapped her way back in the past. Even so I was staggered by her reply. 'Three,' she said.

As gently as I could, I ventured to disagree. I suggested that in today's reality she was actually 20. She winced, and said little more. Most of the time the best she could do was nod, which in her terms meant inclining the head, perhaps a millimetre or two.

The following day Samantha was almost loquacious, at least for her. 'You upset me when we talked about my age.' This amounted to a thorough ticking off. She presumed that if she became upset by my questioning I must surely apologize and back off. I immediately said that I'd had no intention of upsetting her. But I followed this up by asking her to confirm whether or not discussing her age was important. She moved her head almost imperceptibly forwards. I took this as Consent, and, as gently as I could, continued.

Although her medical condition weighed heavily on my shoulders, and a number of the nursing staff were initially most anxious about her survival – I knew I had to talk to her.

This was the road to cure. Terrible things must have happened to her when she was three, for she had, as she so graphically indicated, become frozen at that age. I needed to start from this fact and gently encourage her that adult reality is so much more secure than the nightmarish nursery she had still not succeeded in leaving behind. We began to make sterling progress, during which she began to recount the most dreadful happenings around the age of three, before I was removed from the case.

The Angrier I Am, the Less I Eat

The above story is one illustration of why my fundamental opposition to contemporary psychiatry hardened. The central importance of the emotions cannot safely be minimized. If you can gain the confidence of the self-starver, they will tell you things that make a material difference. For me, fear is the master emotion, with anger a close second. One of my clients made it quite clear that the angrier she became, the less she would eat. The conventional approach would have been to force her to finish her plate, against her Consent. However, as she freely explained to me, though she would comply this time, her anger would grow so much that at the next meal her 'anorexic thoughts' would banish her appetite entirely. Coercion in instances of self-harm is entirely counterproductive.

Suppose, on being admitted to a new ward, you were greeted by the consultant psychiatrist who briskly informed you that, as an anorexic, you had 'something evil inside you', that you had an incurable disease. How would you feel? What if he went further and said that every week he would personally weigh you, having had you stripped down to your underclothes beforehand? Would you feel this invaded your personal space? Would it tend to make you somewhat peeved with such an approach? Granted that the angrier you are, the less apparent your appetite will be, how much success would you expect?

If, as a psychiatrist, you lack the ability to discuss how emotions influence the course of a disease, you can have no notion of which way the component of anger is moving. If your anxieties, the staff's anxieties and those of the customer's kith and kin are allowed free rein, again progress is liable to be hampered. Truth, Trust and Consent must form part of the clinical routine. This may sound counter-intuitive, and contrary to your psychiatric training, but where human emotions are concerned, no progress is possible without them.

Anger and fear underlie all self-harm. And as with all irrational emotions, they are amenable to a supportive approach. Every terror has a definitive cause, and every anger has an underlying context. The key therefore, is to flush these out, to replace them with today's far more secure adult reality. Not always obvious, but, as with Emotional Health in general, certainly available to all.

So far I have discussed one form of self-harm – by starvation. But it is remarkable the lengths to which some will go to damage themselves. Samantha deliberately and methodically scalded herself within minutes of arriving in her new ward. The alacrity with which these troubled souls will burn, scald, strangle, cut or otherwise damage themselves or hazard their lives is astonishing.

The majority of the 60 murderers I treated in Parkhurst Prison had scars across their faces, their arms or their chests. Self-harm is the expression of rage directed not outwardly but inwardly, against the self. It makes no sense. It also makes a mockery of the orthodox medical (and indeed the conventional criminal justice system's) approach: 'Do such and such, or you won't get better.' This is liable to elicit the response: 'Good. I don't want to.'

So much reliance is placed on the efficacy of punishment, yet here are innumerable souls who are already heaping as much punishment on themselves as they can muster. While working in prison I found that many prisoners' view of punishment differed greatly from the norm. What you or I might abhor, they may positively welcome. In a more sensible, less feudal society this sort of evidence would not be suppressed, as mine was, but used to improve our approach to criminality and reducing crime.

It's Your Loss

Despite all however, the origin of all this self-destruction is in fact the same as that of any other irrational emotion – and it is just as curable, given abundant supplies of Truth, Trust and Consent. One of my more painful disappointments over the last three years was being prevented from implementing my plan to eliminate self-harm from the women's unit in the maximum-security hospital where I worked. My plan was straightforward – I would have worked with the nursing staff to build an atmosphere on the wards where the inherent 'lovability' of all was brought out in a convincing manner, just as I had, rather surprisingly, in a maximum-security prison.

So what are the general principles for dealing with those who demonstrably do not want to be well, who wish to starve or harm themselves? The first step is to recognize that all irrational emotions are infantile. Next, to understand that the person displaying them would rather not have them, despite their protestations to the contrary. (They tell you as much just as soon as they grow up.) But these more benign feelings have become covered over with an excess of anger and fear, of rage and terror – and unless and until these can be addressed directly they will take their toll as savagely as any other blind, powerful and obsolete emotion.

The reality with all these troubling customers is that they have never fully appreciated that they are entitled to be Lovable, Sociable and Non-violent. They have never had the opportunity. No one has invited them. They are then systematically subjected to coercion, distrust and deceit, which build up to overwhelming proportions. Despite this, the way through the morass is – build bridges, extend trust, seek Consent. Then the afflicted individuals will come to see that they do in fact have something of value. Their own inherent 'lovability' will out, for the first time.

If these victims can once be convinced that they do have something of social worth, the rejection they have invariably suffered can be stood on its head – they can develop the confidence to say to their rejecters: 'It's your loss.' Without sufficient encouragement or adequate supplies of confidence, this reversal of their fortunes is simply not available – it just doesn't arise.

But when it does, then the blossoming that occurs has to be seen to be believed. And everyone of us can participate in this fruitful activity – not because we are special but because we are human. And the delightful thing is, that as our own Emotional Health improves, so we can better assist others, and they us.

Addictions – Sexoholics, Workoholics, Gambloholics, Heroin, Cocaine and All the Other -oholics

Trying to capture in fixed words what it is that goes so wrong with the ineffable human mind is a major linguistic challenge. It helps to describe the central problem as a mental landmine that is so lethally explosive that its owner does not ever wish to think or even peer at it again in case it explodes. Even if to everyone else the landmine is manifestly a dud, this matters little, since where terror reigns, thought is paralysed.

The problem can also be described using the box as a metaphor. A life-threatening memory or lethal flashback is buried behind massively thick and concrete walls, rather as the tuberculosis germ becomes encased in layer upon layer of fibrous scar tissue, from which it too may break out whenever the victim is at a low ebb. The task then is to convince the customer that the box is empty. But of course to do this they will need to be persuaded to open it for themselves and see. This is where Consent proves so vital. However, opening it is something they resolutely refuse to do – except where there are abundant supplies of Truth, Trust and Consent. Without these, any nursery nightmare is preferable to what they believe is certain extermination in today's reality.

Samantha, for example, was subjected to so much pain and fear at the age of three that she shut the whole thing away, at the back of her mind. Even to begin to consider it meant putting herself back into the terrifying situation which she has spent all her life running away from. The 'terror' is like a furnace, too hot even to contemplate approaching to see if it is now out. And, of course, until she can be persuaded, not coerced, to do so, the irrational torments continue.

Both the landmine and the box are merely strings of printed words which only partially capture the reality of 'frozen terror'. Terror is the most powerful and mobile of the emotions. Words are not good at describing something that is alive and mobile. In Part Five I shall discuss quite why it seems so necessary to stick with the fixities we know, rather than embark on the fluidities that matter – to stay with the dogma we are familiar with, rather than set out to explore what is really important.

This is the challenging background to the addictions. Here we have the most ingenious entity in the entire cosmos, the human mind, insisting on staying blind drunk. It turns itself off. What can possibly be going on? It is like a fit man insisting on being lame, a well woman telling all she is bedbound.

Gary shows something of these problems. After I had been at Parkhurst Prison a year or two I had established a reputation for dealing with sexually abused prisoners. Thus it was that I was asked to see Gary, who complained of fearsome nightmares of being sexually abused, and there were fears of his killing himself as a result.

Again Gary highlights the serious limitations of using punishment to decrease activities of which society disapproves. Gary was serving four years for selling heroin. But his story reveals deeper problems, which this punitive strategy quite overlooks. What Gary told me, when I had gained his confidence, was that he heard voices. In his head, over and over, was a voice saying, 'You're garbage, you're garbage, you're garbage.' Now this was not something that Gary could argue with – the voice was already in his head. So, as with Stan in an earlier chapter, Gary had attempted to drown out the voice by taking drugs, eventually ending up with heroin, which not only failed to work but also landed him in prison.

Now I had been taught in my psychiatric training that what the voices actually said was of no relevance. And were I to suggest in a psychiatric seminar that Gary should shout back at them, I would be laughed out of court. But my interest was in finding the 'frozen terror' which was driving Gary to distraction. So I asked about his childhood. It was not long before it emerged that he had been dreadfully sexually abused by a close relative. When, as I normally did, I invited him to shout at a figment of this relative – to his surprise the voices faded. He became steadily more in charge of his own mind. He was able to assert himself against the abuse which had so damaged him when he was too small to defend himself.

This is where the roots of addiction are to be found. They will invariably be well hidden, because their owner finds the whole area painful. Gary for instance believed that even talking about his abuse would land him back into it. He was prepared to do a great deal to prevent this dire calamity from recurring. Punishing him with imprisonment had no impact on the real problem. Time for a more enlightened approach to penal affairs.

The most obvious addiction is to alcohol. This is a commonplace toxic chemical that immediately befuddles the mind, degrades muscular coordination and has a precisely destructive longer-term effect on the liver and the brain, neither of which we can live without. We all know what damage it does. There have been various coercive and intrinsically doomed methods of curtailing it, notably the Prohibition Era, which sounded promising but produced mayhem. What we are less familiar with is the infinite range of other patterns of distorted social behaviour which serve exactly the same purpose – disabling the thinking abilities of irrational individuals.

Alcohol is the most obvious socially paralysing addiction. The next most familiar are the other commonly available drugs – amphetamines, cocaines, and the various derivatives of the opium poppy, including heroin. All these have in common their ability to deflect the mind from other matters. And what could that be? For all the prolixity, variability and range of 'deflecting strategies' – the one thing every irrational action is seeking to divert attention from is a hidden terror from long ago.

Besides these chemical addictions the human mind is well able to devise a whole series of other 'diversionary tactics'. Indeed anything run to excess can tie up all loose mental resources that might otherwise be left to dwell on intolerable 'pains' and insoluble problems left over from our earlier experiences. It is time to give the human mind credit for creating an infinite array of addictions. A wry smile is always called for when I hear of a new wonder tranquillizer, or other mind-bending drug, which is sold as being 'non-addictive'.

We also have the workaholics – for them work is all-consuming and the pressure that comes from attempting to complete it is ever present, while completion is ever unattainable. The underlying objective, as with all irrational activities, is to divert the mind from the hidden disaster which, if the individual should once make the mistake of stopping to look around, would consume everything without a second gulp.

Next are the sexoholics. For such individuals the diversionary tactics involve members of the opposite sex, or for homosexuals, the same. There is a compulsion to engage in as much or indeed as many sexual encounters as can be fitted into the time available. Each 'partner' on these excursions serves one purpose only – to fill the mind with an 'acceptable activity', to the exclusion of an unbelievably dangerous alternative.

The point to bear in mind with all these addictions or '-oholix', is that for all their infinite variety, their underlying objective is always the same. The victim needs desperately to avoid thinking about a relatively simple, primitive even, item in their mental furniture. In doing so, their first remedy is to throw everything they can at it, or rather between themselves and it, whether that be sex, work, money, chemicals, or indeed any other possible human activity that comes their way. The people practising such diversionary tactics will of course deny it indignantly. They will say that their explanations are perfectly reasonable. But the Truth is simpler and more painful.

All these compulsions are powered by hidden emotions, in particular rage and terror. Until these are assuaged the compulsion and the self-destruction will grind ever onwards, consuming all and everything before it. The only realistic remedy is to unlock the box – something that requires generous supplies of Truth, Trust and Consent. These can only be provided by other members of our Sociable species who are not consumed by irrational compulsions.

After alcoholism, the most poignant addiction is gambling. This perhaps damages as many families as any chemical. Either way, the gambloholic calls for as much social concern and as much remedial activity by society as a whole, as does the alcoholic. Gambling in the UK, has recently obtained government approval, with the national lottery.

Gamblers, on the face of it, enjoy the notion of getting something for nothing – they long to defeat the idea that there is no such thing as a free lunch. But behind the feeling that here is something for nothing, there soon creeps in the notion that gambling provides some way of beating the system, some means of getting your own back. When the odds are clearly stacked against, when your every previous gamble has conspicuously and expensively failed – against all the available evidence, you persist in hazarding hard-won treasure.

One of the more surprising addictions I have seen customers escape into is violence – such an emotive activity that whole armies of terrifying memories can hide behind it. Suppose someone began to imply that you needed to be more independent emotionally. If you felt sore about this, there's nothing like punching him or her to divert the conversation. As mentioned, three murderers much preferred to threaten my life initially, rather than set about unpacking their terrifying memories. Violence is, of course, highly destructive socially, but it also very effectively distances the sufferer from the tender warmth and security through which alone this affliction can be cured.

The remedy for addiction is the same as for any other irrationality – open that box, grasp the dud landmine and cast it away. These are empty words until they are implemented in the here and now. And I repeat that these painful points must be approached with extreme caution, for addictions are powered by enormous emotions, which for all that they are infantile, retain huge energy, which can destroy more than just the addict.

Coercion seems to be such an obvious way to approach those who are addicted – but it misses the point. I well remember the first time I worked in a Drug Addict Unit, in New York State in 1965. This special unit was housed on the fifth floor of the only modern building in a large mental hospital. Security was high – access to the unit was by a special lift, which had a unique Yale key to open the lift doors, and a different key for the unit's door. The higher the security, the bigger the challenge to the inmates. No hospital routine could exist which did not include daily walks in the grounds. It was during these walks that the various caches of drugs were surreptitiously retrieved. Security represented a challenge to be breached. The solution is to seek out the hidden 'frozen terror', as with Gary, and turn it off. Only in this way can this socially damaging problem be cured.

There are many schemes and projects whose purpose is to tackle these destructive activities. Clearly those that work with the sufferer, engaging as much Truth, Trust and Consent as is locally available, will tend to be more successful. Indeed those that increase the autonomy and self-esteem of the sufferers will fare better than those that leave these points ill defined. The objective, as with all moves towards Emotional Health, is that the individual becomes more mature, in other words that they grow up emotionally.

100

Part Three –

Problems With Others

Part Three – Problems With Others

8 Curing Family Strife

Evidence from Evolution • Why Hurt Those You Love? • Cutting the Roots of Family Frictions • What Are We Like? • Ensuring You Get More Fruitful Help from Others • Negative Self-esteem, Negative Social Skills, Negative Futures • Fighting Parental Figments • Why Love 'em – then Leave 'em? • Pulling the teeth of Domestic Violence • Hitting the Wrong Target

Let's review Emotional Health from basic principles. Being Healthy Emotionally means that our minds and emotions start doing what we want, and not what they seem to want. It means that we call the tune, we remain cool, calm and collected. The pay-off from this is that our social networks improve. One requirement for achieving this objective is to understand both what we want and what we can reasonably expect. Because if things are not going right, then clearly we must have got our wires crossed somewhere – either we don't really want it or what we want was never on the cards in the first place. Some believe we could never hope for anything good anyway – altogether too pessimistic for my taste.

In Part Two I discussed how emotional problems could arise within yourself, which basically turns on how Lovable you perceive yourself to be. If you are unlovable, you are at risk from a whole range of unpleasant things which you scarcely notice because you feel you don't really count or you are not really there. This is not always an easy problem to mend, but the second axiom of Emotional Health states that we are all born Lovable, so we are all entitled to aim for this and indeed to expect it in others we meet.

As we start Part Three, Problems with Others, the main issue revolves around the question of 'Sociability'. Are we born Sociable? Well, if we are not, we are certainly in a deal of trouble. The axiom states that we are a Sociable species. If we are, this has impact on all our social institutions. If it is once accepted that we are born Sociable, we would spend far less on locking people up in our disgraceful prisons and far more on programmes for socializing our delinquents. As it is, around two million people in the United States are deliberately socially degraded as a matter of public policy. One in four of all the world's prisoners is a citizen of the US of A. In the UK we are catching up as fast as we can, and already have more life-sentence prisoners than all the other European nations put together. Smacking or physically assaulting those smaller than you was until recently endorsed by our school system – hardly proficient training for ensuring family harmony later.

Evidence from Evolution

Now let's take a step even further back. Homo sapiens is the only mammalian biped – we walk on two legs, unlike any other creature, anywhere or at any time, that also suckles their young. But you cannot run as fast on two legs as you can on four. If we cannot run away from our predators – what can we do? Why have we been so evolutionarily successful? We have sacrificed fleetness of foot for manual dexterity which is a bold evolutionary move, akin to the dodo giving up the luxury of flight. When the seafarers chased that flightless overgrown pigeon, they extinguished it with ease. Is our terminal factor going to be our refusal to acknowledge our 'sociability' and our insistence that the main threat to our survival comes from other humans? We have assuredly accumulated enough thermonuclear weaponry to extinguish any number of biospheres.

Sociability therefore has biological, even medical, implications – do it or die. Indeed 'sociability' has a firm evolutionary basis. If it is once accepted that we are indeed, at base, a fundamentally Sociable species – then wherever we find unsociability we should take steps to eradicate it. Doing so persuasively would benefit us all.

Nowadays we humans have social contacts on a wider scale than ever before. We start with the family, go on through the local community, next the nation, then the globe – at each stage we can either assist the social weal or undermine it. And if 'sociability' is the key component of our evolutionary survival strategy, the more we promote it, the better our chances of surviving – and the less, the worse.

Why Hurt Those You Love?

Suppose when you come home you find yourself picking petty arguments and needling those closest to you. Assuming we are a Sociable species, this is less than optimal. Something has happened that has deflected your particular domestic situation from being a socially helpful one to being a socially harmful one. Something additional has come into the picture. It no longer stands to reason. Why do we hurt the ones we love? Well, for one thing they are the nearest and the most readily available. For another, we don't have to be very brave. It is easy for grown men and women to cane small children – they have the power and the strength conspicuously lacking in their impressionable victims. And there is little risk of any comeback. In our curiously feudal country there is no legal challenge, or at least only a weakened or recent one.

If we find the mind carefully doing the wrong thing and striving to avoid the only logical conclusion, clearly this is irrational. And, as with all irrationality, we need to look for the mental landmine and that fearsome box. It is entirely irrational to move warmly towards someone while at the same time inflicting harm upon them. It can only occur because of misperceptions. We hurt those we love because we do not see them, or us, clearly. We do not see that being Sociable actually pays. And we do not see this elementary, even primeval, fact, because we are burdened down with other, more terrifying matters.

The one thing which makes no sense is to 'explain' the problem by labelling it 'love/hate'. This is a non-starter, a contradiction in terms, and it deserves short shrift. What it really means is that you hate them, but daren't say so. And since fear is the master emotion, under every hatred lurks a fear. Thus if you find yourself excusing your destruction of your nearest and dearest by labelling it a 'love/hate' relationship – you need to think again. There is more fear there than love, and in all cases there should be more 'sociability', not less.

The trouble with all emotional tangles is that you cannot see them straight. They are there, they have a certain reality. But to see what that is – for that you need a modicum of self-confidence and a notion of what should really be going on. And, of course, to gain more confidence, you need a better, more productive social support network in the first place.

So here is another explanation for why frictionful social relations grind on indefinitely. What is needed is for each party to get a boost from the other, so that there is less tension, less fear. Only then can 'sociability', mental peace and calmness come into the picture. But what tends to happen is that Trust evaporates – 'You always do this or that

– you cannot change for the better.' Further interaction is persistently counterproductive, and the way to better Emotional Health is blocked by festering emotions and habits established and unchanged over a lifetime.

Take this on a wider scale. Why are so many anti-social individuals, such as prisoners, deprived of the opportunity to learn better social skills? Why lock them away from the social contacts they are already having difficulty with, incarcerate them with thousands of others equally socially inept, deny them the opportunity to rectify their social deficiencies and then insist on hampering their social rehabilitation on their return to 'freedom'. It is not logical – so it must be irrational.

We all want safer streets and less housebreaking. We all want less violence. We all want a more secure environment, a more stable society. And we all know how to get it – but we perversely insist on doing things the way we always have, and end up with the worst of both worlds.

What applies in the home applies in our wider society and vice versa. We are frightened of violent criminals and of criminals in general. But instead of pursuing rational policies to eliminate violence and criminal activity, to reduce it to negligible proportions, we continue with repressive, coercive policies and strategies, which leaves the central problem untouched. Indeed, it inevitably makes it worse – by actively disabling their Sociabilities. We perversely seem to prefer punishment to eliminating the anti-social problem itself.

Of course, if we really were innately Sociable, and all anti-social acts were aberrations – we could work towards a common goal of increasing 'sociability' all round. The beauty of this approach is that everybody gains – it is a real win-win situation. Homes are happier, we stop hurting the ones we love, we cease making social unrest actively worse – and we make the world a safer, more secure place, whether on a one to one basis, or in our wider society. And the way to do this is for Emotional Health to become a much more urgent priority, not only for ourselves, but for everyone.

If you want Emotional Health, you can only get it by being Lovable, Sociable and Non-violent. Provided there is abundant Truth, Trust and Consent then the inherent benignity of humanity can blossom. And it does.

Cutting the Roots of Family Frictions

The prime context in which we all wish to be Sociable is our immediate family. When families fall out, the agony can become long drawn out. So families are the ideal place to establish Emotional Health – except families are private. They have their own rules. They do things their own way. And why not? Privacy is precious, increasingly so in this intrusive age. This means that the call for remedies has to come from within. Given the axiomatic status of Consent, there is no other basis for proceeding – not if you want to do less harm than good.

Families are where we first learn about this curious species we have just joined. There are adults around with their own particular foibles, other adults who visit, some more often than others. Then there are the children, some bigger than us, some smaller. And so life begins – a rich variety of sunshine and showers, of balmy emotional interchanges mixed with acidic, obstreperous ones. But all the time there are human contacts to acknowledge, new customs to observe. What this entails is maintaining good diplomatic relations with as wide a social circle as you can.

But families are also where we first learn our hidden agendas. In our earliest experiences there may be some issues which are too much, for which there is no immediate remedy – and these become buried. A family with buried and unseen horrors is a family at war. A toddler who is punished too hard may remain fearful for ever. A seven-year-old can conclude from a fearsome remark that there is no hope for later success.

Being a 'thinking' species, we survive by remembering what happened last time, so as to avoid it next. We learn to pick our way gingerly around a prickly relative, whether parent or visitor. We learn not to do this, or not to say that, in the wrong context – and if the explosion has been a big one, we learn this prohibition at considerable depth. We may confide this 'secret' to one or two others in the family but circumstances and circumspection generally conspire to divert us from confronting the irascible individual too directly.

So it is that family myths are formed. Factions build up, fears breed, petty hates ride piggyback on larger, better hidden volcanoes of negative emotion – and in the maelstrom the goal of all families is lost. Where families should be the cornerstones of stable, civilized societies, they become festering social sores which can all too easily spill out into the neighbourhood, and infect and corrode other, happier families.

The real tragedy is that the 'damage' which underpins the festering sore, as with all irrationalities, is long gone. Once exposed to today's harsh reality, it would vanish without trace. The original fear took its roots from an insecurity, a perceived snub or rejection, which, even if perceived realistically in the first place, is now long past the stage when it could do any harm.

As with all such 'memories', if they are not ventilated promptly, they can take on a life of their own. They then elicit further deceits, distrusts and coercions. This feeds back into the original circle, cutting off the nearest and most immediate supply of emotional comfort and support. Where those closest to us should be the most supportive, because of this obsolete breach, they are the very ones who interact least.

When family feuds have festered too long, they become self-sustaining. For example, in times gone by, both the Scottish clans and the New Zealand Maoris had repeated battles amongst themselves which were essentially family feuds writ large. Members of the opposing clan came to be seen not as potentially fruitful members of the same species but as variations on a diabolic variety of a creature best avoided.

The two world wars can be seen as originating as just such another family feud, this time between Queen Victoria's grandsons. Wilhelm wept for his beloved grandmother when she died in 1901. He competed with his cousin, George V, which, in the monarchical structures reigning at the time, sufficed to trigger a global catastrophe. Wilhelm didn't like to feel the poor relation, so he built as big a navy as the one that ran the British Empire. He was not functioning in a vacuum, but in a closed family rivalry. George himself was equally susceptible to family strife, he actively refused asylum to his other cousin, the Tsar of Russia, who met a grisly end as a result. Families at war cost us all dearly.

It is striking to see how the ordinary soldier in the First World War better fitted the axiom of being born Lovable, Sociable and Non-violent than is generally realized. The majority of rifle shots were fired into the ground, because killing others was not what the foot soldier really wanted to do. And the famous Christmas Day football match, which so horrified the High Command, demonstrated 'sociability' above strife.

What Are We Like?

One of the continuing casualties of the First World War is the damage it inflicted on our perception of ourselves and our neighbours. In the late 1800s, there were no passports restricting travel throughout the world. Governments did not control or coerce their citizens, who could come and go as they pleased – Consent was the order of the day. Even in the aftermath of the Franco-Prussian war of 1870, Robert Louis

Stevenson's travels in the war zone were free, if somewhat foolhardy.

In 1911 the British government passed a ferociously worded Act, supposedly to combat the possible presence of German spies in Britain's midst. I have personal experience of this same Official Secrets Act. In 1997 it was used in an attempt to destroy video evidence that the prisoners I had been treating in Parkhurst Prison had human feelings and failings, like the rest of us – and wished to re-join, or in some cases join, the rest of the human race. It is sad to see that irrational fears still impede the present government's moves toward repealing this deplorable Act.

Lost in the maelstrom of the two world wars is the notion that human beings are fundamentally benign. They prefer to be Sociable rather than hostile and wish to engage in friendly activities rather than destructivities. Given this background, this backlog of mutual deceit and distrust, it will require considerable positive mental resources to reverse the trend.

Human beings need to be seen as Lovable, Sociable and Non-violent. And the evidence to the contrary needs to be counteracted, so as to change the ethos to one that is more benign. What should be self-evident from the nature of human evolution is rejected on ideological grounds, much as blasphemy was in an earlier era, and its proponents subjected to restrictions which, in a healthy democracy, would be quite intolerable.

The problem is that the more you don't see, the more 'evidence' you accumulate that what you think you see is real. If you are a professional expert and you have spent your life climbing to the top of your particular tree, you are unlikely to take kindly to some interloper suggesting it is the wrong tree.

Human beings have long been anti-social towards each other. What evidence is there that they have changed? Or indeed that they can change? What is needed to convince is adequate supplies of Truth, Trust and Consent – for without these, then the dearth of confidence which characterized the irrational and unrealistic assessment in the first place is likely to remain unbudgeable.

So what is the remedy?   How can family strife be cut at the roots? The key to undoing family wars is the same as that for undoing both civil and global wars. Having lived through a bombing war, I like to comfort myself that if there was ever a war between, say, Japan and the United States, the Japanese would never bomb Manhattan the way the Allies did Berlin. The reason is simple and pragmatic – they own too much of it. That is to say, they have too much to lose.

And precisely the same reasoning applies to families. There is more to be gained in every family by emotional interchange than by endless bitter recriminations. What is essential is a context in which communication is available. If you freeze someone out, you are cutting yourself off from a supply of delight and creativity. I should say a possible supply – since hard prejudice will promptly inform you that such individuals in the opposing clan are not to be trusted, understand nothing but coercion and couldn't tell the Truth if it hit them in the face.

Prejudice is rife, and carries its own penalty. A penalty which is exactly proportionate to its depth – the deeper, the worse. And the remedy is always the same – communication. Talk to the opposing clan, see them react in remarkably similar ways to those you are familiar and comfortable with. Discuss whatever issues you can.

And remember, there will always be a welter of arguments from all directions which avow that the hated faction never change, can never change. Endless citings of the wicked and evil things they are alleged to have said or done can keep you on the edge of your chair. And you must evaluate this as best you may. But if Emotional Health is on your agenda, don't lose sight of the most optimistic assessment of what human beings are really like, or wish to be like. And help and support others who are moving in the same direction – there's nothing like a support network to start undoing the worst excesses of the opposing clan.

I would not wish to give the impression that human beings have suddenly become angelic. But the impression I certainly do wish to convey is that each of them, whatever their past, can move decidedly in that direction. But to do this, they may each require considerable encouragement, if not example. With such enlightenment, it is possible to spring miraculous changes from the most unlikely quarters.

A cautionary tale is perhaps in order. In the run-up to the recent wars in the Balkans, a Yugoslav policeman walked up to a newly erected roadblock and began discussing its sensible removal with his friends who were manning it. 'Look,' he said to them, 'I am unarmed.' They shot him.

There are always pitfalls. And there is precious little that can be done when the antagonists are consumed with terror, and thence with hate. Terror paralyses the mind. But the fact remains that human beings, for all their irrationality and violence, were born in a happier state than many now find themselves – and it is up to the rest of us to assist them to return there.

During the last few years, as I developed the approach described here, and tried to discuss it with my colleagues in psychiatry, my career suffered. When I worked with some of the most dangerous prisoners in Britain's prison system, I made a point of telling them that I could not help them if they frightened me. This is what fear does. It colours the mind, it paints blacker pictures than are really there. But when the mind clears and confidence returns – it becomes possible to distinguish those circumstances where it would be foolhardy to try anything further from those in which just one more push, one more attempt at persuasion, will open the floodgates of warm, friendly feelings, in which we can all refresh ourselves.

It is sometimes a nicely balanced judgement, which way to play it. But in all cases the inherent benignity and intrinsic 'sociability' of human beings is always there, however hidden, for those with strong enough intent to seek it out.

Ensuring You Get More Fruitful Help from Others

If you want to find out whether or not we are born Sociable, go somewhere where everyone concerned has made every conceivable effort to extinguish it. If you don't believe we have within us an ounce of benignity towards our fellows, the best place to explore the Truth of the matter is where the expectation is dominant that we are born unsociable, even anti-social. And that this anti-sociability is absolutely 'untreatable', and where the (unwritten) instructions to the staff are to act as if this were the only applicable axiom in the case. Such an environment is daily enacted in our prisons.

The most anti-social act is murder. If you live in a primitive country, all you will do is shut the murderer away for as long as possible, and try and forget all about it. You may also arbitrarily extend their sentence – and if you have an especially unscrupulous Home Secretary, you make a point of doubling all remaining sentences while you are in office, without regard to due process of law, justice, fairness or any notion of attempting to leave the world a safer place – which is what criminal justice systems should really be aiming for. This happened during the time I was at Parkhurst Prison. What I found especially hard was when Michael Howard held forth at the Tory Party Conferences, referring to the prisoners as if they had no hope of change and deserved only ever more punishment. Punishment makes matters worse. Brutalizing criminals can only increase crime. Certainly the Home Secretary made my job harder – perhaps that's why he closed the unit. What struck me as odd was that no one in authority or in government effected to notice anything untoward.

The level of civilization in a given nation can be gauged by how it treats those who kill. If you sanction legal execution through the use of capital punishment, you are endorsing the notion that human beings are expendable. You pay no heed to the suggestion that we are all born Sociable, and deep down would wish to return there. You have no truck with the argument that 'sociability' is our chief evolutionary survival mechanism. Every legal homicide you sanction is not so much a step closer to the jungle, an evolutionary fermenting vat, but one inch closer to that ultimate evolutionary sanction – species extinction.

So if you have doubts about our being inherently Sociable, the best place to explore that proposition is in our prisons. Here you will find all those who the rest of us wish to forget. They are already anti-social and they have had heaped upon their heads more unsocial abuse than you could normally imagine. It is not terribly logical – your crime is being anti-social, so we will show you how to become more so. A better word for such nonsense is not illogical, but irrational.

The strange thing is that, if you do spend some time with these dreaded dungeon denizens – they teach you things you only half knew or just didn't know at all. But they will only do that if they trust you. They will only respond in a warm, human fashion if you approach them in this vein. And they won't even do that to begin with. They simply don't know how. They have never been taught. They have never seen it before in their lives. If you ask them about 'sociability' before you begin, they are even more convinced that it does not exist than the most inhumane jailer, or the most purblind minister of justice or Home Secretary.

Thus when I arrived in Parkhurst Prison in July 1991, I knew that my main challenge would be to unearth problems from childhood terrors. What I found was that the prisoners had been exquisitely trained to malperform. They had been pointed exactly in the wrong direction, into patterns of behaviour that would achieve precisely the opposite of what they wanted. So if you think you hurt the ones you love, or you drive your energies up a blind alley – you should pause to see how it is really done.

Negative Self-esteem, Negative Social Skills, Negative Futures

It did not take me long to realize that my prison clientele exhibited negative self-esteem, negative social skills and negative futures. They knew they were scum – they had always been taught that, they had never known anything else and they regularly expected the prison system to continue their degradation. Why should they expect anything else? They knew they deserved nothing better, indeed, if you asked them straight, they judged they deserved worse. That was what they were accustomed to.

They were also highly skilled at achieving the very opposite of what they wanted. They asked, often vociferously and at the top of their voices, with threats and much malice aforethought, for what they didn't want, and never once for what they did. Asking for what they wanted had never worked in the past – all the signs were that it would currently be used against them, so this too was a non-starter.

Finally they had no futures. The present was bad enough, the past even worse – why should they expect any better from the future. Quite apart from their being burdened down with more 'frozen terrors' than you would want to meet in a year – they simply had no incentive to look beyond the immediate, to modify their behaviour so as to benefit from future gain. No wonder they remained emotionally hamstrung – Emotional Health was not even a pipe dream.

Now if you could detect a change in such a population, if you could observe that these 'forgotten souls' began to show feelings and propensities that were not there before – this could hold out hope for the rest of us. For if such benighted individuals can remedy their self-assessment, can throw off all the shackles their previous Emotional Education has thrust upon them – then who is there who cannot?   If it worked for them, who will it not work for?

So if these fragile, brutally abused individuals with personalities so diaphanous you can virtually see through them – if these thoroughly disadvantaged men can begin to gain more fruitful help from others – it would be wise to find out how they did it, and follow them. Not, of course, that the prison system, which was built on the opposite assumption, could tolerate anything of the sort. The Special Unit was closed as swiftly as possible, despite the fact that it was doing entirely successfully just what it had been set up to do – Key Performance Indicators were applicable only for use by other departments in the Prison Service but not in C-Wing. In parenthesis I would like to record my thanks here to the late John Marriott, then Governor of Parkhurst Prison, who initially held back from me the tidal wave of repression. Without him I would never have dreamt of working in such a place, indeed I would never have been allowed even to cross the threshold – rather as I am not now.

And the pathway which proved so successful there leads directly to the axiom of Truth, Trust and Consent. My work at Parkhurst Prison proved to me that we are all born Lovable, Sociable and Non-violent – and that is precisely what these prisoners began to display, much to their delight and the Home Office's chagrin.

Not everyone has the opportunity to spend five years in this way, learning what makes human beings tick – nor is the present prison policy likely to permit any such thing again in the foreseeable future. And fewer and fewer of us are killing each other than used to be the case – not that this reflects any merit on the way our criminal justice system handles such appalling problems. But there are lessons to be learnt, if only there was enough social confidence to do so.

Negative social skills are all too easy to acquire. You fear something, you think crookedly about it and you bellow your worst fear out loud, thereby facilitating its coming to pass. It is like fretting too long and too loud that there may be a tiger in the orchard which would prevent us collecting all the fruit – thereby ensuring all the fruit rots, with or without the predator's presence.

Here again we see the master emotion, fear, in action. Clearly, if ever we are to reach a higher stage of Emotional Health than before, fear is the number one target – we need to reduce it, as we managed to do in Parkhurst Prison, by spreading around as much as we possibly can of Truth, Trust and Consent.

The negative social skill which afflicted Sigmund's father, causing him to bellow at his impressionable son, had repercussions throughout Sigmund's life, and indeed for myriads of individuals who have carefully been taught Freud's own restrictions on parental critiques. Throughout his life Sigmund never came across anyone he trusted enough to talk through, and thus dispel for ever, this hidden terror of his father. How could Freud therefore have any confidence in a brighter future?

There was no way that Freud could appreciate where his irrational fears came from, nor could he conceive of ridding himself of them – accordingly we have pessimism here on a grand scale. Happily for those of us who are concerned with curtailing irrationalities and pursuing Emotional Health, there is a limit to the number of hidden agendas that so corrode our passage through this challenging world.

Freud had two priorities. The first was to try as best he could to sweep clean the Augean stable of irrational, destructive and degrading emotions which so afflicted his patients. This he could see and pursue with a single-mindedness and a clinical acumen that has rarely been exceeded. The second, and ultimately the more powerful, he could not see. He could not see it, because it appeared to him that it paid him not to see it. He did not, on this analysis, want to see it – and being a powerful individual, he was successful in this regard. It would have helped us all if he had been just a little less successful.

This second agenda was hidden. In simple terms it amounted to wrestling unclearly with his father's destructive instructions. This course he could only pursue blindfold – since discussion of the reality of his father's assessment was not available to him even to think about. Had it been so, then he might have addressed his father somewhat as follows – 'Even if I do come to nothing, as you so vehemently prescribe for me, then that is your loss. Besides, whether I do or not, is entirely a matter of personal judgement, in this case mine.'

The widespread effects of such a hidden agenda might lead you suppose that there was a multitude of causes behind it. Happily, there is only ever one. In my experience, if you can reach out and persuade the afflicted individual that there is one box whose lid they need to open, then they will gratefully reap the benefit of proving to themselves that it is now empty. On a few occasions there is another, or a false bottom to the first – but by that time the victim is well aware of how he or she rid themselves of the first, and usually tackles the second with much better heart.

Because we are bipeds who suckle their young, our offspring spend a lot of their early years learning. If they learn that they are failures, that they will come to nothing – then unless they can throw off this yoke they will fulfil the prophecy. Of course, if you can reassess what you have been taught in infancy then you can ease away any problems you might have from negative futures, negative social skills and even a touch of negative self-esteem. The best recipe for doing that, as advocated here, is to seek abundant supplies of Truth, Trust and Consent, and set about, with renewed optimism, ensuring you get more fruitful help from others – that, after all, is what Emotional Health is all about.

Fighting Parental Figments

We all love a wedding. We throw our hats in the air, or at least we used to do when we had hats to throw. We wipe a brief tear from the eye – we all still have eyes, and a tear or two – though tears are not always as readily available nowadays as perhaps they should be. We give a little sigh, or at least those of us who are not too battle-hardened, do. And we wish them well on their happy voyage through the rest of their lives – or we used to do. Whatever happened?   What insisted on going wrong?   Where did that evil serpent in the Garden get the Apple from?   Why are more divorcing now than ever before?   Did the wind change and start blowing us all apart?

If you want an irrational paradox par excellence, take a look at marriage. All those wonderful heart-warming promises – I'll be there for you, I'll help you and you'll help me. The words Truth, Trust and Consent don't usually feature too prominently in marriage ceremonies these days. Perhaps they should, but then again they might not help all that much, if they did. For there is a snake in the grass, a serpent in the Garden of Eden. There is a plughole down which far too many of these entirely laudable, admirable and eminently attainable goals, dreams and objectives sink without trace. There is a third party at the feast, a Banquo's ghost at the reception – and its name is parental figment.

Before we go any further, I have to declare a special interest in the matter. I am a parent. I have children, and now grandchildren. I even have two parents still alive at the time of writing. All this family is a delight to me. I am not out to blame everything on Mum, or to castigate Dad. If I did, I would be obliged to start with myself – because if I were a parent bringing up my children today, I would do a far better job than I managed at the time. This plea must be the standard grandparent's plea – and is likely to be given short shrift – but it goes to show that it is not parental intention which causes so much trouble – it is parental anxieties. I suffered from a number myself. The real word for anxiety is, of course, fear. And if you cannot see that fear, as I could not at the material time – how can you stop it infecting those you love?

So let's exculpate parents. Most would not be seen dead inflicting an iota of harm on their little one's head. If we were not capable of producing and bringing up dependent children successfully, our species would have died off aeons ago. There are some parents who inflict horrendous damage, to all appearances deliberately. There are many more who inflict damage inadvertently. The point to emphasize is that it is not the parent today we are struggling with – for the most part they could not be better pleased with the situation. No, it is the parent from long ago, the one who got locked in the box, frozen there by a childhood terror, which, as we have seen, is not always so easy to dislodge.

Freud features so loudly among today's therapists, too many of whom continue to inflict his dogmatic failures on a wide public, that examining these serves a double purpose. Suppose you looked at the world through Sigmund's eyes – what would you see? You would see your family and your work, you would progress matters as best you could, and you would deal with problems as and when they arose, to the limit of your capability. But at the back of your mind, hardly visible to the naked eye, is something else. Or, to be strictly accurate, someone else.

We know who it was in Freud's case, because he inadvertently tells us. He didn't know he was telling us, else he would have disguised it in some way, as he did from himself. It was his father. In April 1896 Freud had felt free enough to write, with exemplary lucidity, that the cause of sexual abuse and other emotional turmoils was 'pseudo-hereditary' – that is, these problems were transmitted through the family, not through the genes. In other words, paedophiles are taught what to do – which is exactly what I find to be the case. His father died on 23 October 1896, when Freud was 41. Thereafter he could no longer contemplate criticism of parents, even those who had left residual terrors, as in his case, which needed the light of adult reality to dispel.

So he took with him, on all his psycho-analytic travels, a hidden presence – it was his disapproving father, it was his parental figment. The remedy was for him to face the Truth – his father had been terrifying, but was no longer. Indeed he was no longer alive. This Truth however, he never acquired enough support to face.

Why Love 'em – then Leave 'em?

If you drew up a normal contract with someone else, as between any customer and any dealer, you would each contribute something to the agreement, and because it was mutually beneficial, then you would both have an interest in seeing it through. This is perfectly straightforward. There is no hidden agenda. Both parties benefit, so both commit themselves, and the outcome is greeted with satisfaction on both sides. Onlookers, in so far as they are involved, have no quarrel with the arrangement. If the action looks especially fruitful, perhaps they might like to join in.

So let us take the most significant contract in your entire emotional life. They don't come any bigger. You decide that you and your chosen partner will launch forwards together, tackling life's difficulties and joys as a partnership. Even without all the fairy-tale trappings, it does not on the face of it seem such a bad bargain – you get what you want and he or she gets what they want. The notion of mutually beneficial emotional support cannot be bettered this side of Armageddon.

You start to put emotional capital into the project. You rearrange your affairs so that you can devote more time and energy to ensuring the marital arrangement is a success. Everyone benefits from this. Your parents, even your parents-in-law. Your grandparents, if they are still around. And of course, everyone knows that children thrive in a harmonious, well-balanced, stable and, above all, long term relationship between the happy couple.

With so much hanging on it, with so much to lose if it crashes – what the Dickens goes wrong?   Because whatever it is, it has to be enormous. Everyone wants it to succeed. Everyone and his dog is willing the thing on from the sidelines. 'Come on,' they say, 'get your act together – don't go splitting up, for Heaven's sake. That way, we none of us win. We all lose.'

The irony is, of course, that the splitting couple also know full well what is at stake. They know what the losses are, and what the gains were going to be – they were in at the start, remember. So where is the snake in the grass? Who is it that wills this whole venture to fail? Whoever they are, they have a deal to answer for.

Well, I will tell you at once who is not to blame – and that is the parents today. They, more than anyone, know what trials and tribulations life brings. They are desperate for the patter of grandchildren's tiny feet. They've seen it all and they know how lonely life can be, and how much it takes to build a reliable, trustworthy, consensual relationship.

No, it is not the parents today that queer the pitch – it is the parental figments from long ago. Leftover, neglected, pushed to the back of the mind, these dread figments seep out, and rot the whole arena.

And this is where irrationality takes its heaviest toll. Here is a contract, a plan against the hazards of the future, and it is wrecked for irrational reasons. Irrational emotions creep up and immolate the happy union. They colour the partner's face, they distort the perceptions of what is really going on. And unless they are tackled head on, they tend to win. For terrors, as we have seen, whatever their origin, paralyse clarity of thought – and if you cannot think clearly, then you are liable to put your foot, fair and square into it, smashing all around you and reducing all to rubble.

The tragedy is that if only this 'long ago' influence can be seen, put on the table in today's daylight, then it is seen for what it is, an obsolete nightmare. Children are routinely upset, they are frightened, they fall over. Most of the time they are supported – comfort is immediate and readily available. Any fears that might have been there are dealt with on the spot. But sometimes they are not. Sometimes they fester. And when they are bad enough they paralyse their own removal. Then the damage is indelible. It recurs with the next partner, and the one after that. Open that box and blow the lethal cobwebs away – not always easy, but an infallible remedy once applied successfully.

One of the earliest catechisms I used to subject my customers to, when marital problems loomed, was an adaptation of the old biblical wisdom, from Genesis Chapter Two. As with all remedies for irrationalities, it is simple, and it is obviously the Truth. When you are a child your parents are the most important emotional supports in the world. Without them you will most certainly perish, something of which as an infant you are very well aware.

Now when you marry, as the Good Book says, you cleave to your spouse. You leave your parents and you do a spot of cleaving on your own. The question then to ask is, are you a daughter or a wife? A son or a husband? Because on the answer turns your future. And not only your future, but that of your entire extended family.

Now, of course many, many people can happily answer, 'Both.' They are untroubled by irrational emotions, whether fear, rage or terrors, and they sail through life without a care. Their family relationships are all sweetness and light, and all around admit it is a positive pleasure to know them.

However, for others the course of true love is not quite so smooth. There the misperceptions of a mother can become transferred so that they colour the wife, or the misunderstandings of a father can disfigure the husband – sometimes all four occur at once. No wonder emotions have a field day, no wonder some of the most precious things in your life are smashed.

If you could only see what a gorgeous bride your wife makes, or what a handsome and oh so reliable groom your husband makes – then you would surely plight your troths, pledge your hearts and go the whole hog, without further ado. No one could blame you. But what the outsiders do not see is the catch. What the outsiders do not see is the box, the misperception, the landmine at the back of your mind. They don't see it, but then neither do you.

If Emotional Health means anything it means that when two people get married they want to get married, they want to wed, they mean all those extra-special promises. What they don't always see is the left-over baggage, the detritus from earlier family training – and if they cannot see it, then the risk of its tripping them up is just too great. This is where irrationality exacts it highest cost – nursery nightmares become reinstated. Oh for abundant supplies of Truth, Trust and Consent, so that a healthier reality can take over.

Pulling the Teeth of Domestic Violence

If you came across a man who was cooking his wife's supper and every now and then reached out and threw a handful of mud into the pot – what would your reaction be? Or a woman, who was putting up some bookshelves for her husband, but, instead of just fixing the brackets, hammered extra nails all over the shelf – what would you think? It might cross your mind that you were in Alice in Wonderland country.

The whole matter would not improve if these two individuals reacted strongly to your remonstrations. If you suggested that there was a better way of proceeding, would you be surprised if they took no notice? What would you think if they assured you, vehemently, that their partner always liked their stew or their shelves that way – it was what they were used to and indeed what they preferred.

Well, the first thing to do is lay down some ground rules. You can indulge in all sorts of unorthodox practices – provided you do so with Consent – but once violence is involved, then crucial issues are raised for our wider society. Privacy is a privilege and must usually be protected. However, violence against the person, whether husband, wife or child, is always a crime – or in all civilized countries it certainly should be. One advantage of endorsing the axiom of Lovable, Sociable and Non-violent is that it shines a brilliant light into a dark corner – from it you can always conclude that where you find violence, you have found something wrong.

A wife may get angry with a husband and vice versa. This can be healthy, as discussed earlier. But no wife is ever entitled to hit her husband, nor the other way around – this breaks the fundamental Rights of all human beings. And the only way through domestic crises is to seek out and emphasize the humanity of the other party, and the desirability of harmonious emotional support that each can give the other, as in the initial bargain they struck when they first set out together. Just because they happen always to behave towards each other in a violent way – this line of reasoning cannot possibly provide any justification and should be thrown out of court without further ado.

If your childhood family indulged in violence as a matter of routine, then it is hardly surprising that hitting people has a well-established place in your social vocabulary. This does not mean it is healthy. As with all other irrationalities, violence today is invariably an echo of violence in the past. Thus hitting your partner is a sure sign that you are misperceiving them. You are not seeing them as they really are.

Hitting the Wrong Target

Violence, as with all irrationalities, arises through misperception. The target you are aiming at is not the one you are hitting. The problem is that you are today lashing out at a nursery nightmare from the past and must therefore still be living in it. Not a comfortable position to occupy, and one from which your partner would be delighted to rescue you – if only you would give her or him half a chance.

But since you cannot see the problem clearly in the first place, then you are not going to be the most avid customer for its resolution. Again, it needs calm, confident quiet, where you can slowly re-evaluate the most important emotional relationship in your life, and set about ensuring that it delivers more comfort than bruises, more cuddles than broken skin or bones.

Domestic violence flares up and enflames many of those who seek to assist. Whereas the bruiser is labouring under a childhood illusion, many of those who rush in to help also bring their own hidden agendas with them. There are even some partners whose misguided emotional education has led them to suppose that, unless they are hit, then they don't really 'count'. Perhaps in their childhood the only parental attention they received was violent. If this sounds entirely strange to you, be thankful for that – for when you listen to the childhoods of the most violent men in the prison system, you hear enough in this vein to make you blench.

At root, domestic violence is starkly simple. She or he does not think they are Lovable. And after s/he has hit you once or twice (once would suffice for me), then doubtless you are eager to agree with him or her that s/he is not. If the danger is too great, then you must seek outside help. 75 per cent of all murders are committed by people close to you.

But this 'Lovability' issue won't go away. It must be addressed. If you come into adult life and you have doubts about who you are, what you are like, and in particular just precisely how charming you are to other people – then this issue must be rectified before you go any further. Of course, it does not help to hit those who think (or are trying to think) you are wonderful. This tends to force the issue in the opposite direction, reinforcing your social handicaps.

I suppose it is possible to construct an argument along the lines of 'If I didn't hit him/her, then our marriage would collapse'. But this is fundamentally upside down. If you want to hit something, go find a tree or a rock. On the other hand, if you want a human relationship that might assist you – then you need to see that human beings are really rather curious creatures. They respond most favourably to persuasion and Consent, not pressure and coercion. If you want a supportive emotional network, then the only people who can possibly provide it are people who like you, people who Consent to be with you. Coerce them and you lose all your customers, as we noted in Part One.

Lovability is the first issue. It is not always easy to unpack such a deep rooted problem – but it is certainly possible – indeed with enough support and adequate input, then success is guaranteed. But it can only be done by Consent. Waving a bigger stick, or in the case of the criminal justice system, a bigger punishment, makes matters worse, at considerable cost to all concerned.

It helps if the axiom of Lovable, Sociable and Non-violent is adopted, since this provides the basis on which to excavate the 'lovability' which underlies us all. The next point on the agenda is 'sociability'. Clearly violence is anti-social. It is never anything else. This is one of the reasons that violence is a disease – it destroys social structures, it erodes mental supports and it vitiates peace of mind and mental securities. What else do you need in a disease? Tuberculosis does exactly the same to our bodily organs, and no one doubts it's a disease.

Violence is also a learned disease. It is not inherent in us when born. You can argue this if you wish. But why did those prisoners in the Special Unit in Parkhurst Prison change within a few years? Did they have a surreptitious gene transplant when I and they were not looking? If they did not, then they must have changed of their own free will. And if they could change because they wanted to, then there is nobody in the entire world who cannot do the same, provided they are prepared to work at it and have the right recipe and ingredients.

But it is not my job to force this conclusion through. Since Consent is a component of Emotional Health, then you must agree or not agree to these points, as you wish. However, if your partner is attacking you or you are attacking him or her, be advised this is not a healthy situation for either of you. It is a disease situation. And there is a remedy. It is a simple remedy – though not invariably an easy one. It involves Emotional Education, it involves relearning what human beings are like, what cuddles and comforting is like. It requires that you be convinced you are Lovable, that you benefit by being Sociable – whence Non-violence follows as day does night.

In these troubled waters, fear plays its usual confusing and unsettling role. Violence is frightening – that is why it is such a staple on our televisions. Violence emotes, and what emotes sells. But there is more to it. The beaters, the bruisers, the grievous bodily harmers – these are cast as the villain, which indeed they are. But they also lose out. They are not the victors, they do not hold all the cards. Pyrrhic victories are the only ones they have.

If we and they can hold aside the tidal currents of fear, and can see what is really going on, what is really going wrong – then a rather sorry picture emerges. The violent individual is a seriously handicapped person. One of the serial killers in Parkhurst gave a dismal account of his earlier marriage, when he was 19. At that time he appeared to have all he wanted – his food was cooked, his laundry done, he had as much sex as he wished. But, he said, he could not talk. If there was an argument or a discussion, he 'talked' with his fists. He could not describe his feelings, his emotions – these were not available for conversation. It was only after we had managed to clear away whole cartloads of intervening fears, terrors and rages that he came to see his earlier situation in its true context. He had been bereft – and whereas he still faced a lifetime in prison, at least he now saw human beings as Sociable and Non-violent.

He taught me and I taught him. This is a mutually beneficial relationship. He was the one who commented on the difference between a four-year-old's tantrum and that of a 24-year-old, which was his age when I knew him. He came to see how he was missing out, how his inability to feel, to exercise his emotions, was a major disability and one which he was quite delighted to shed. Now, if he could do it, then who cannot?

When moving into these difficult and challenging areas, the question immediately arises – is what I say True? Is my account trustworthy? And of course everyone has their own view. My own revolves around the unfashionable notion that we are all born Lovable, Sociable and Non-violent. But since I do not offer any coercive proof of this axiom, you are entirely at liberty to discard it. It's just that if you happened to show a passing interest in Emotional Health, then it is the only recipe I know. And if you are inclined to believe me, I heartily recommend you try it out for yourself.

9 Restoring Amicable Family Relations

Are Parents Human? • Do Parents Need Us? • Who Did You Marry? •
Childrearing and the Parental Dilemma

Families – don'tcha just love 'em, love 'em to bits! Always the same – get them in the same room and they are instantly at each others' throats. Squabbling over this, scrabbling over that, moaning, whingeing, whining – she has a better goodie than me, he has a better sweetie – and that's just the adults. When it comes to the children, why it's enough to make you throw up your hands in the air – but what with?   Despair? Well hardly, these are your own flesh and blood, these are those you grew up with or whom you grew up. Cut them off too savagely and your heart might not only ache, it might bleed. But what a price we have to pay. Those rascally emotions – they certainly take their toll.

We all have parents, generally two. And unless we achieve some sort of distancing from them, then we are liable to spend the rest of our lives repeating their mistakes. But why should there be so much rancour?   Why all this heightened emotion?   What is it about families, and especially about parents, which brings out so much fierceness and misunderstanding?

Well, it is all to do with our prolonged and utterly dependent childhood. For the happy few, this proceeds idyllically – your parents are understanding of your every whim, no great catastrophe strikes, they have gained sufficient independence of their parents to decide things for themselves. This matters, because being complex as we are, the problems we face are always just that crucial bit different from those our parents led us to expect. So when adulthood arrives, these cheerful few sail through untrammelled.

For the rest of us, the problems begin shortly after we learn to walk, if not before. We adapt. That's what living organisms do. We find out as much as we can about where we are and make as much sense of it as we are able – and we adjust our behaviour and our expectations accordingly. In the middle of all that is going on there are our parents – the most important souls in all the world. Without them, as our emotions never cease to prompt us, we would cease to be.

So we place them where they deserve to be – right at the heart of things. And there they tend to stay. Which is unfortunate really, since everything else moves on, one way or another. We establish an excellent life-support system, we learn our way around the things, or rather the people, that matter most – and if conditions become inclement, we tend to stick with what we know – parents.

But then, time passes. We change. Our surroundings change. Our responsibilities and our capabilities change. We have new challenges, we have a spouse, possibly some children – all these make demands, ask awkward questions, pose challenging problems. We grow bigger. But do we also grow up?

It is highly reminiscent of our birth – the umbilical cord which attaches us to our mother is cut within a few minutes of birth. If it is cut too soon, our life is endangered – but if it is not cut at all, then our life is intolerably restricted. Precisely the same applies to our emotional umbilical cord, but being less tangible and therefore less obviously in need of severance, it can linger far longer than makes any rational sense. So we make irrational sense of it.

Are Parents Human?

For infants, every parent is a superwoman or superman. This is entirely as it should be. For without this, the infant perishes. And of course in terms of size, capability, power, persistence and perspicacity there is nothing that can remotely hold a candle to them – from an infant's viewpoint, it is not too much to say they seem like gods. Above all they are the suppliers, and thereby the possible withholders, of life itself.

But the reality is different, not necessarily more mundane, but markedly different. Our parents are people, just like us, though necessarily somewhat older. And since reality is where we all now live, then we need to see all the other inhabitants as they really are. Thus parents may have once been god-like – but really they are only human, with as many foibles, faults and fantastic talents as you or me.

Though this may seem logical, rational and obvious – not all our emotions will agree. Growing up emotionally is not always as straightforward as it should be. The real difficulty comes when we seem to have grown up, we appear to be strong, straight and independent – while all the time, hidden away in a dark corner of our mind, we are still only seven years old, or thereabouts.

So we face our adult challenges in two minds. We are dancing to two tunes. The one powerful, highly charged, energetic and altogether blind and therefore unrealistic – and the other, proportionately less well endowed with energy, seeing all too clearly the havoc, the mess which we sometimes do not have the strength and self-confidence to curtail. These are the infantile – and the nascent adult.

Happily for our rational selves, and our understanding of where our powerful emotions go so wrong – there are only ever two such tunes. And once we grasp this, we can begin to sort the adult sheep from the more infantile goats. We can patrol our mental furnishings and boot out those that are well past their sell-by date. This again is something that Freud, and too many others, simply do not believe is possible – they live in a fully determined universe in which *che sarà sarà*, what will be will be, and we have no 'intent' to vary it. Thus the infantile fate becomes your adult fate and your infantile terrors haunt you even into your ninth decade of life.

But there are serious differences between what an infant can do and can expect, and what is available to an adult. These differences are not small, nor finely detailed – they are gross, obvious and unmistakable. Unless, of course, you have a vested interest in mistaking them. Then of course, all the differences in the world are as nothing – they are even more invisible to you than the back of your head, since you resolutely decline to look in any proffered mirror.

And the key change turns on the role that parents play in your life. An infant is dead without them, but an adult survives better by seeing them as ordinary people. Parenting certainly keeps infants alive, and adults insane. Parenting means doing everything for you, feeding you, cleaning you, keeping you warm and comfy – without parenting when you are an infant, the future is horrific and brief. However, an adult needs self-confidence, self-reliance, self-control and the ability to take responsibility for yourself. Every parent has the obligation to bring you up, and to bring you up to look after yourself – not an easy double act, but vital to adult mental health and Emotional Health.

So parents need to change, they need to transmogrify from huge to normal, from super-powerful to everyday, from giant to human, from central life-giver to background supporting role. Often they are more than willing to do this. But their offspring bug them – they keep coming home to suckle, which they learnt hard and deep was the only way to survive. Who'd be a mammalian biped?

So it is the offspring that need to change, though often this is easier said than done. But do-able it certainly is. The really curious thing is that so many just never think it. It never remotely occurs to them that their parents are ordinary people – in some ways better, in some ways worse, just like the rest of us. It never even enters their head that they can re-evaluate something that was set in mental concrete decades ago.

But when it does, the thrill is more telling than a flower bud opening, more fascinating than watching an eclipse of the sun, more enthralling than seeing a duck egg hatch – for it confirms to both parties involved that we humans can change, we need not be slaves to our past. We can flourish and blossom, and set about increasing the world's store of Truth, Trust and Consent – thereby bringing benefit to all.

Do Parents Need Us?

Having spent so much emotional energy winkling ourselves out from within the tight emotional umbilical circle that we all start off with, it may seem odd to turn the question around and ask if parents need us. But the point is, we need to be realistic, we need to live in reality, that is where we either survive or we do not. And the fact is that parents are just as human as anyone else – so can enhance your supplies of Truth, Trust and Consent should they have a mind to it, as well or as badly as anyone else.

But the emotional tags which hang on to parents are fierce and loaded, as befits any other life-support system. And if these remain hanging around, then 'normal relations' will not be resumed either shortly or indeed ever. If when you see, talk to or even think about your parents, your liver quakes, your stomach turns over – then have a care – you may just be touching on something that is decades old and shouldn't really be there at all, not any more.

There is nothing wrong with being 100 per cent dependent on parents, or parent type figures – always provided you are very, very small. If you are big and behave small, then stand by for serious trouble.

I had thought to include some 'exercises' here, some hypothetical situations upon which to ask you questions. But I am not too sure it would be a good idea. Better perhaps to try and describe the blueprint as clearly as possible, from more than one viewpoint, so that you can get a good enough idea of what the aims of Emotional Health should be, and how best to set about getting there. The difficulty in my stirring up, or setting out to stir up, obsolete emotions in your 'back memory' is that it might get out of hand. Were you on the chair in front of me, as Sam was earlier, then I could gauge what I said to suit the situation. As this is now unlikely to be the case, time and space being what they are, then perhaps a gentle amble in the general area might be the most prudent. Bear in mind that some of these very early, very primitive life survival strategies are deeply ingrained and difficult to shift, even with your full-hearted Consent and understanding – there is nothing so mysterious as the human mind, even yours.

Bear in mind too that we are not talking parents today – we are talking parent figments. These are past parental images, or memories, set in mental cement, which need levering out and throwing away, from both your own viewpoint and that of your real parent today.

Your parent today, unless too much bile has passed under the bridge, will be as keen as you to be amicable. You can guarantee that it will not work if either of you misperceives the other, even by a hair's breadth. This is landmine country. Unless the landmines are clearly visible and everyone knows for an absolute certainty that they are duds – then one or other of you will be on tenterhooks, and the mayhem of the standard family gathering will obtain, as before.

For what the family squabbles are about is not today's details, but yesterday's life or death. Your parent today has no more say over whether you live or die than any other neighbour – but if you think he or she has, or your emotions are determined that s/he does, then do not expect a calm and settled relationship. Only through emotional maturation, or Emotional Health, can such an admirable circumstance be guaranteed – which is what reality is all about.

Who Did You Marry?

If your marriage is fine and dandy, then you are one of the lucky ones, and yours is unlikely to become mangled in the ever gaping maw of the divorce statistics. But if it is not and you are worried about various creakings and groanings emanating from the foundations, then check out the misperceptions.

As with all other irrationalities, misplaced marital emotions need to be handled with considerable care. Irrational emotions as described in Part One are invariably life-size, as befits any other life-support system. And you may be sure that if two people see enough advantage in joining together in a partnership, only to find after a while that the goods on display at the start are not what appears to be the case later – then something has gone seriously awry.

It is unlikely to be anything obvious at all. It is highly likely to be something that has shown up only in passing. The purveyor of irrational emotions denies that they 'own' them. It pays them to have no knowledge of them whatsoever. So if things are beginning to go wrong, or have been going wrong for a time – then the central cause is likely to be entirely invisible. Or if it begins to peek out from behind a whole lot of other verbiage that might, just might have something to do with the root cause, then its owner is likely to stamp very hard on it, or on you, to ensure that it remains hidden.

Don't forget that a life-support system that consists of hiding things away will not relish being wrenched out into the open air, especially when what is being so furiously hidden is a gigantic figment. As with any landmine, better not go too close, you never know what might happen next. And if you don't know, then it is safer to keep quiet, and not find out something that perhaps you would rather not know.

But let us take a robust view. Two people who settle down together, with or without a marriage certificate to authenticate it, must have had some reason for doing so. They must have thought that this was a good idea. They must have seen some advantages. Others may pull their chins, wag their heads in a knowing way, saying they suspected it would never work out. But they are guessing. They cannot know what went on between the happy couple at the start – or if they did, then it was none of their business – whatever happened to privacy?

No, the basis of the first contract is likely to be entirely valid. Two people can live together, supporting each other, and striving to achieve that most desirable of all ends – mutual emotional support. Nor is there any inherent reason why such an arrangement should not work as intended. It is unreasonable to suggest that men are forever wandering off, or that women are at base fickle and unreliable. Two adults can decide on a contract in marital business just as reliably as they can in any other commercial or social transaction whatsoever.

There is no difference in the terms of the agreement, openly and consensually entered into. But there is substantial difference in the delivery. If the emotional roots are pointing the other way, then whoever you married, or however you struggle to mend the gaping holes that appear – if one or both are pulling back into the past, then it will not be easy to repair. For the problem with emotions is that when they go wrong, when they take off without their owner controlling them, then the root cause of the problem is hidden. It is not available for analysis or inspection.

Once it is, and there are ways of bringing it gingerly out into the open, then it can be seen for what it is – an obsolete nightmare, with no more relevance today than last year's fish and chips.

But before this happy state of affairs can be reached, it is essential to uncover what the misperceptions were at the start. If you 'thought' or misperceived that you were marrying some sort of reflection of your long-ago parental figment – then there is little surprise in the fact that the actual person you are now living with is not like that at all.

If you can once gain this realistic perspective, then this is your partner's supreme advantage. As before, they are then in a uniquely capable position to spring you from the remnants of your nursery nightmare.

One of the ways of exploring this is to try a spot of gentle probing. I am reluctant to be too specific about this, for I am well aware of the huge emotions involved, and how they can swoop down like some giant vulture and carry off all remaining domesticity, if they once get out of hand. So enter the following arena with great circumspection. Have some moral supporters on hand, if not actually in the room with you. Above all accumulate as much Truth, Trust and Consent as you can lay your hands on.

If these precautions sound over the top, and all goes smoothly – then thank goodness. If they do not, then you have gone too far, too fast and the holes in the marital fabric may be even more difficult to repair. I speak from considerable experience of irrational emotions rearing up in enormous proportions like some fearsome genie out of a bottle – so go gently. Nothing is to be gained by coercion or trickery. Indeed much is to be lost by that route.

We are cautiously approaching your foundation stones. These are the very basis on which you are who you are. They constitute your first line of defence when stress begins to build. You normally keep them tucked safely away at the bottom of your mind, where they sensibly belong. The only conceivable justification for disturbing them, or even thinking of disturbing them in the least degree, is because they may be upsetting the real world out there, and you want a more stable, more fruitful marriage than the one you currently have.

So here's the question – who is your priority – who's your next of kin?   The answer to this is the same as given in the Book of Genesis, mentioned above. You leave your parents to cleave to your spouse. The law backs this up by declaring that, legally, your next of kin is your husband or wife. Well done the law, I say. For your emotions should be entirely in accordance with it. Your first priority, your very nearest and dearest, should be the one person you have elected to live with.

So what was all the fuss about?   Why all these long faces about explosions and so forth. What could be more straightforward, simple and above board?   What indeed. Didn't I always say that the remedy for irrational emotions was the Truth. That shining the harsh light of reality into the gloomiest, darkest corners of the roots of irrationality was the best remedy of all, the most reliable way to see them off the premises permanently.

 And so it is. The problem is that, if you want to hide an even deeper priority below the one that shows up on the surface, then it's your mind and you can do what you like with it. You may indeed say, and know as far as you can, that your priority is where it should be. But emotions have ways of tricking you, of showing you one thing very loudly so that you can avoid looking at something else.

Now there are two things going on here. One is I am suggesting that someone else may know more about your mind than you do – not a very polite thing to suggest. And the other is that I may be suggesting problems and dangers which simply do not exist, they are not there.

To counter the first, we must emphasize the notion of Consent. Whatever others, myself included, may suggest – whether you accept them, consider them or even listen to them at all is entirely up to you. Without your Consent then they are merely wasted air, or in this case paper. So Consent is crucial.

Next, the evidence for these dark, irrational secrets comes from the here and now. It does not come from anywhere else. If you are 100 per cent content with your current domestic emotional arrangements, then this particular discussion of them has no relevance whatsoever. But, and this is the problem, if there are symptoms at the surface, the place to look for them is in these cellars below.

The problem is always the same – there are parental figments stuffed away at the bottom of the box. The remedy is also always the same – gradually, and, I must stress, entirely in your own time, you lift the lid and find the box empty – that is my confident prediction – thereby blowing away the roots of any irrationality and the burdens of any childhood remnants that might have gone along with them.

I suppose the preceding paragraphs could seem rather puzzling. On the one hand there appeared to be great peril in the offing – on the other, nothing to worry about at all. Well, this in summary, is what irrationality is all about. The danger is entirely fictional, figmentary and in the past. But the danger is that the individual victim of it does not see it that way – they see their life-support system being arbitrarily threatened or even thrown away, without there being anything at all satisfactory to take its place. Whence the anguish, the emergency emotions and the outpouring of panic.

In reality, today is a secure place for an adult to be, without a parent in the background to hold their hand, supply their succour and defend them from nastiness. And when you and your partner can both see this, and agree it, then the future prospect is indeed rosy.

So many evil, dangerous and fearsome events have overtaken humanity in the recent past, that it is quite likely that doubts creep in as to what human beings are really like, or indeed what they are capable of. Well, the view from here is that humanity is fundamentally Sociable. That means we function best in relationships.

The problem is that in order to be Sociable in a fruitful, rejuvenating manner, it is first necessary to be Lovable. If you do not believe that your personality, the very essence of you, is something of value, worthy of some esteem, then you are not going to believe in the deepest sense that anyone would value living with you. And if you don't believe it, no amount of reassurance that this is what your partner has chosen to do will impact on this deeper negative within you.

So the first criterion for living happily ever after is to know 100 per cent that you are Lovable. If you haven't brought this with you from infancy, then get some assistance, accumulate some Truth, Trust and Consent, and work at finding out how others evaluate themselves, and join in.

Next, unsurprisingly, is the notion of you both being Sociable. Again this needs to be established as a given, an axiom. This is not something that might immediately spring to mind – humanity's inhumanity has been on the go at least as long as we have. So asserting that we are a Sociable species may not attract an immediate positive response. However, there it is

– and the more support for this axiom, the better. Perhaps I should admit a personal interest in this axiom – my survival, as a member of the species, is just as tied up with it as anyone else. I believe that 'sociability' is Homo sapiens's secret weapon in the evolutionary survival stakes – so I am rooting for it. It also happens to augur so well for happily married relationships, which is all to the good for those who really would like to live happily ever after.

Who said Emotional Health was dull?   If it can assist in bringing this type of miraculous fairy tale a bit nearer, if it can offer reliable guidelines to this effect – then more power to its elbow, say I.

Childrearing and the Parental Dilemma

Let's start right at the top with the 'parental dilemma'. This is a dilemma which afflicts all parents, and indeed others who are called upon to deal with immature individuals – and its horns are razor-sharp. Fall one way and you do harm, fall the other and you inflict damage. What a life – who'd be a parent?

The simplest illustration is holding a toddler's hand. Say you have a two-year-old, or thereabouts, and you come to teach him or her to walk. To start with, nothing could be easier. You take a tight grip of their tiny hand, walk confidently up and down with them – and everything is sweetness and light. You are not worried, they are delighted to be doing something new, something challenging, something more 'grown-up'. So far, so good.

But then what?   You can't keep doing that all day – but the pressures to maintain the status quo are considerable. You are comfortable, they are content. You are in charge, you say where you both go, you pick the route – nothing can go wrong, because you can see to it that it can't. Why quit when you're ahead?   There are powerful attractions of staying as you are – you are in control, they are entirely safe, at least as safe as you can make them – and your responsibilities in all respects could not be better fulfilled.

But there's a problem. Whatever life is or does, it moves. And it moves on. Unless you let go of that infant's hand, then he or she will never learn to walk. Here's the other horn of that dread dilemma. Do you want a walkless child?   Can you really contemplate a lame duckling?

You know all too well that as soon as you loose go of that tiny hand, as soon as you devolve your responsibility for locomotion to what previously has been entirely your charge – then disaster could strike. You can readily visualize, as an infant cannot, split heads after a fall on the sharp curb, broken limbs as they trip on the carpet, or worse, blood and gore as they tangle with oncoming road vehicles.

The horrors are there, just round the corner. The temptation to keep a tight grip, so as to avert them, is large. Seductive notions well up – things are not really that bad the way they are, at least they are safe, at least no harm can come to them – and so on and so on. The 'reasoning' is endless, but the dilemma doesn't even flinch. If you don't let go, they will never stand on their own two feet – and though the consequences of that may not seem great from where you are standing, in due course they can be savage in the extreme.

Put the same dilemma at a later age. You are teaching your offspring to drive the car. You sit in the driving seat, you sail through the traffic, you anticipate the road hogs, you edge into the right lane – you know what you are doing, you've done it before, you have no problems. But that's not the issue, that is not the point of the exercise. Your offspring knows you can drive, he or she also knows that they cannot – and the longer you delay, the more agitated and impatient they become. Eventually the time arrives when they sit behind the wheel. That's the time when the agitation abruptly transfers from them to you. You know that the first lamp post suddenly develops an irresistible magnetism, the car in front looms alarmingly near – disaster threatens from all over the place – no wonder you preferred the earlier scenario.

This dilemma arises because we are autonomous individuals, or at least we need to be moving steadily towards that, as we become ever more adult. We are not automatons nor robots – not if we wish to remain sane, that is. But we need to learn, and we can be taught. Those who teach us can either be quietly confident, and thereby successful at devolving these various life-hazarding skills – or they can be frightened and frightening, and thereby unsuccessful.

Fear is the master emotion, and here we see it skipping back and forth, from those in charge to their charges and vice versa. If you attempt to resolve the parental dilemma by instilling fear, either with verbal or physical abuse – then what you are in fact teaching is that the task to be learnt is itself frightening, if not impossible. If you can persuade yourself to put the rod away, break it for preference, then you will have a better chance of saving that child from a fateful robotic future.

This is essentially how the precept of Consent needs to be responsibly applied to children. If your child, or any other immature individual in your charge, is about to come to harm – you have two choices, as before. You can force the issue, or you can seek Consent.

When the child is really small, as when newborn, nothing is simpler than whisking him or her up in the air, away from all possible dangers. At that age, you put them down and they stay put. Nature has endowed them with neonatal quadriplegia for reasons which are not entirely clear, and so any moving about that is to be done has to be done by others. We are all born without locomotive ability – we need to learn how to do it and then what to do with it – not always the easiest of progressions.

The parental dilemma is fairly blunt to start with. Children go where you say. Their self-determined locomotion is non-existent – what you say, goes. But from their first wriggle your days of 100 per cent control are numbered. If your strategy is to rely exclusively on your deciding their location, then you're done for. And if devolution does not go smoothly, so are they.

A newborn waves her limbs purposelessly. That is the nature of things at that age. A toddler, on the other hand, moves about. You cannot predict where. No one can. This upsets many academics who wish to tie our knowledge tightly down – but that's the reality. You simply do not know; a point touched on in the Introduction and again in Part Five.

So back to that choice – your baby is about to come to harm – what do you do? Well, at first, there is only one option – you force the issue, you sweep them up in arms many, many times stronger than theirs, and you control their geographical status 100 per cent. There is little point in asking their Consent because even if they did agree, they cannot implement their part of the bargain – they are quadriplegic, remember.

But then they begin to wriggle, they begin to put their foot to the ground, they start out on their life's journey, which inch by inch continues to their grave. And here we have one of the central curiosities of life – they move under their own steam. This is where the parental dilemma begins to bite. You know where they should move for the best. But they are the ones doing the moving – only feebly at first, but better and stronger as time passes, until eventually they are as good at it, if not better than you.

Imagine the grief, the havoc that would be caused if you decided to stop the clock, if you decided that you were their chief traffic controller, they could go only where you elected – thereby continuing the neonatal pattern long past its safety zone. It happens.

So, as the 100 per cent control of the neonate lapses and becomes obsolete, what are you going to put in its place? The danger is still there, still gaping its maw ready to swallow feckless chicks without trace. Well, the answer depends on what you want. If you want to be unrealistic, to pretend that there is no such thing as progression, that the past is exactly identical to the future and always will be – in this case, you may continue coercing as long as you have the strength. In some ways this may seem the easiest option, the most appealing – might is right.

In reality, and if you hanker after Emotional Health either for yourself or your dependants, then the rockier road, via Consent is your only sensible, rational alternative. Tricky, risky and by no possible means certain – but in the long run, even in the fairly short run, if you do not engage it, then you can kiss mental and social stability goodbye.

But this means going counter-cultural – today's culture after all, is essentially coercive, with the issue of control being central. In the Victorian era it was widely believed that children should be seen and not heard. The damage such a repressive precept does to mental confidence and Emotional Health is incalculable. Children may be difficult to listen to, time consuming to hear, awkward to argue with, exasperating to persuade or dissuade – but if you stunt their abilities for exercising their inherent intent, their powers of Consent the damage you do can last through countless generations, and often does.

From an evolutionary viewpoint there may be advantages for our offspring in having a long, slow developmental period. But the difficulty is that if you were brought up wrong, even only in certain respects – then you tend to 'know' that that is how children should be treated, and you treat them that way, willy-nilly. I did.

And the biggest element that is so often missing is Trust. You don't know what it is, what it is for and how it works, if at all. And again, this must be seen to be believed. If you have never seen it, or never seen it at work – then how are you to know how crucial it is? How indeed.

One of the intriguing techniques which modern technology allows, is to place an earpiece in a parent's ear and guide them in their interplay with their child. The child sees you and responds as usual. They do not hear the advice. To the outside observer the mismatches in your joint expectations are readily apparent – a single comment can produce wonders, not to say miracles.

Your child gives you a quick glance, a once-over, as we saw with the tantrumic child earlier. You may not notice. He or she then continues, depending on the information he or she has just acquired. The outside observer comments that you might be more generous, that you don't need to draw back quite so far, that if you offer something that it did not occur to you to offer, you might notice a difference. The child already has a picture of what to expect – if your guided reaction confounds that expectation, stand by for a radiant smile bright enough to melt even the most frozen prejudice. When Trust blossoms, we can all bask in its glow.

We are considering how Trust and Consent operate between parent and child. But this process is no different from that which operates between any two or more humans, or doesn't. With children it is physically easier to ignore what they want, what they intend. It is relatively simple to shout louder than they, to quell their comments, to disguise their Consent.

But the challenge is the same. Do you Trust them? Have they ever experienced trustworthiness. Do you know what it is, so that you can show them? Or is it something that you need to learn too?   Parenting after all, is a skill like speaking that needs to be learnt.

They are like the advance guard who sees round the next corner for you – you cannot be everywhere. The prescription says – increase their autonomy in graduated stages, so that they can feel the responsibility on their young shoulders, lightly to begin with, but then ever more heavily until their burden is no different from yours.

Share your fears, disclose your anxieties, discuss the options – this can start from day one. Infants may not be very verbal, but they have powerful emotions, as we have discussed, and these need to be fully taken into account. They can also assess your emotions, sometimes better than you. So here is another pointer to taking them fully into your confidence. Truth, Trust and Consent may sound a little advanced for a mewling incontinent infant – but start.

For then, as they grow and when they are adult, you can all share in a win-win situation – a prospect available to us all, with a little Emotional Education.

10 Relating Better at Work and in the Neighbourhood

Coinage Is Not Everything • Buying and Selling • Imperishable Values • What to Expect from Friends and Other Emotional Allies • Why Should You Care? • What Neighbours Are for – Building Social Support Networks • We All Need Kith and Kin • Why Poverty Matters • My Benign Thread

The quickest way to scrutinize the impact emotions have on work is to look at those without. Work, that is, not emotions. 'Gizza job – I can do that' was the catchphrase of a hard-hitting television series when Thatcherite economic policies were at their height, hammering the poorest. Unemployment was then, as always, a serious social disease.

What would you do with your day if you had no structure to it? Have you got schemes that you would happily pursue if economic constraints were removed? Or are you dependent on external structures to 'get you going', to move you out into the wider society?

On the face of it, going to work is all about finance. If you don't, then you have no money to pay the bills. This is true enough at one level, but it doesn't cover half of it. Money is important, indeed it has profound social and emotional implications which I touch on later. But it is not sufficient – much else is involved.

We are social animals. We survive, in an evolutionary sense, because we work together to meet the various challenges –

environmental, nutritional and anarchic – which threaten our stability if not our survival. In the various financial and economic structures we have devised over the millennia, we now have a means to transmit or communicate our various energies and input over wide distances of both space and time. But the central human characteristics have not changed – we still need social contacts, we still need to build our support networks and to contribute to our communal well-being.

It is a major strategic challenge for policy makers to create the best match between those economic levers we can control and the requirements we all have that are inherent in our humanity. It is challenging to devise better economic precepts which relate more to the latter than to the simple, indeed somewhat banal, accumulation of ever more spondulicks.

The central task of the human mind is securing fruitful social contacts with other members of our species. As a matter of fact, this turns out to be a valuable social function. In the better-organized societies, therefore, it carries a distinct economic reward – economics encourages what we would prefer to do anyway. The more realistic the economic policies, then the more favourable they will be to helping fulfil something which happens to be the central task of us all anyway.

Work can be a drudge, but there are actually ways of either automating it or paying, or being paid, a premium for it. Human beings like challenges. They love engaging their mind and deploying skills they have acquired. And the range of the latter is infinite.

We develop a 'good feeling' when what we do benefits others. Quite how good, and quite how widely we define 'others', varies from person to person – the wider the better. For we earn our self-esteem, and our self-confidence grows as we interact with our fellows. And we need to have a supply of these essential social ingredients, whatever our economic circumstances. Even the richest of us needs human contact, and even the poorest cannot survive without it. The remarkable thing, given the heavy prejudice that attends financial wealth, is that these human requirements transcend all barriers, whether of race, age, religion, gender or, as in this case, finance.

The acme, of course, is to bring to our work as much of the element of creativity as we can. This is by no means a simple task. It involves thinking something new, something that was not there before we started. But when we achieve it – those around us relish it as much as we – which is what 'sociability' is all about.

The notion that we are all Lovable and Sociable at heart tends to wear a bit thin in the daily grind of everyday work. Those we work with seem at times to be operating on a different wavelength. Perhaps they haven't heard the good news – perhaps they've heard all about it and have robustly concluded it is a load of old codswallop – and who can blame them? Some seem curiously reluctant to give, give, give – though all too happy to take, take, take.

Now, when you are faced with this sort of down-to-earth bolshiness, then you might be forgiven for supposing that human beings have lived past their acme and that they are now operating in a different world from that to which they have adapted in evolutionary terms.

My own work situation, as described earlier, was clearly less than perfect – but this does not mean that we are all condemned to work in the emotional equivalent of Antarctica or the Black Hole of Calcutta. Besides, even then, I did manage to improve my working conditions – admittedly only after I had left my original unhelpful colleagues – but nevertheless I was able to greatly ameliorate the circumstances in which I carried out my medical duties. And, above all, I was able to learn from my customers. It was they who finally taught me that the one thing they didn't want to think or talk about was, in fact, the most important emotional fact about them. Had I not had their unstinting moral and emotional support over two full decades – I should never have come anywhere near this. 'Frozen terror' would have remained where it has always been, and is intended forever to remain – hidden away undisturbed and undisturbable, at the back of the mind.

So even though my professional colleagues were unhelpful, my lay or everyday colleagues, that is, my customers, went miles out of their way to help. They acknowledged the efforts I was making, they thanked me for the troubles I took – and in general they gave me lashings of straightforward moral support. They trusted me. And slowly I learned what I needed to know. Slowly I inched my way forwards to where the real action was – and then in September 1986 I hit the jackpot – or rather the most important medical customer and I uncovered what we both had up to that point not wished to see.

And this has been my experience in other tight corners. Where my colleagues have been scratchy and destructive, my customers have rallied round. And this, after all, is what work is about – if your customers do not benefit from what you are doing, then something is seriously wrong. If you are in an ordinary market place, then no customers, or no satisfied customers, leads steadily to no trade, and thereafter no trader.

So the people who are supposed to benefit from the work you do – these are likely to be more appreciative of the efforts you make on their behalf than your less perspicacious colleagues. And, in the ultimate analysis, customers matter more – for without them, your business ceases to exist.

So how would you set about bringing these more cheerful notions to your work? Where would you get hold of the energies and the processes that might improve the Emotional

Health of your workplace? What levers would you need to pull to ensure that at least these notions gained a foothold?

Well, the first item, as always when trying to sell change, is Consent. There is no way that a coercive solution will work. Persuasion is the name of the game. Of course, you could always bring to everyone's attention the enormous gains to be had in the way of productivity when the workforce are cheerful, cooperative and non-bickering. Time and again these rather elementary human values are demonstrated to improve the health of the company's balance sheet, which, when coupled with an improvement in the health of the staff, is a double benefit.

 Why should it be such a surprise that the human capital in any work situation does a better job when its humanity is taken into account and given a steady infusion of support? It stands to reason that the more cheerful people are, the better they relate to each other, and, *ipso facto,* to the work they do. And, to return to the first axiom of Emotional Health, to work better we all need adequate supplies of Truth, Trust and Consent.

There are closer parallels too. In Brazil there is a famous industrial experiment which insists on increasing the democratic component at work. The management relies explicitly on Consent – and the company thrives. In this country we have innumerable negative examples of where the opposite applies, and productivity falls.

But the real impact of democracy is the greater shafts of realism which it can shine into troubled corners. The eruptions of irrationality which so hamper productivity arise, as always, from mistraining in the past – they are directed to fighting battles which no longer hold any real threat. Daylight dispels them.

If you can sit down, in a neutral setting, and put your cards on the table – then the problems of today will be seen in their realistic context, and the irrational prejudices from the past can at first be identified as such and then steadily erased. What you need is a confident neutral facilitator – someone who is not in the original context, who has not yet been tarred with the brush of either faction or clan. He or she needs to know what they are about, and above all needs to have the Trust of all concerned.

Even though it may not always be easy to secure sufficient Trust, or an individual with enough confidence to hold the meeting together – then at least the blueprint towards which you are all working should be clear and agreed. The item being produced should be the easiest to agree on – whether it is more widgets, healthier patients, brighter students, better services, cleaner streets or fewer paupers.

All need to agree that the main obstacle is irrationality. And that the chief agency responsible for this handicap are past fears – which again, Truth, Trust and Consent can remedy, by promoting Emotional Health.

Money plays a large role in work. But it is by no means the only, nor always the prime, player. Human beings are curious creatures – they respond to some things more than to others. At heart they respond best to warm emotions, since these presage support and longevity. At times the notion that we are all born Lovable, Sociable and Non-violent may seem as distant as the far side of the moon – but if you can once begin to make it pay, if you can once put it to work – then the pay off for all concerned, especially yourself, is little short of miraculous.

Coinage Is Not Everything

I was brought up under conditions of material scarcity. It was wartime. Food and clothing were rationed. There were ration coupons for meat, fat, flour, sugar, eggs and then cheese – all were in desperately short supply and were only available on production of the appropriate rectangular clippings from ration books, printed on low-grade paper. Fresh fruit was a rarity. And for a young child, the most critical was, of course, the sweet ration – only _ lb. (120g) a week. But otherwise, at that age, all this 'grown-up stuff' made little difference to me. I still remember, at around the age of eight, being dumbfounded by my confrontation with my first banana – it decidedly got the better of me, since I had not the least idea how to open it – such a humiliation.

The nutritional health of the population during that time was better than at any time since. There is some evidence to suggest that the British responded better to this planned economy than other European nations – and that this had a material impact. For myself, I well remember hearing a lecture by an Old Scholar who looked like a Painted Lady. She was festooned in furs and larded with cosmetics – an unusual sight for a schoolboy in 1954. This self-important individual lectured us on her experience as a high status official in the Food Ministry during the war. She still expressed her disapproval of the idea of rationing, which went ahead, so she told us, against her express advice – 'I told them it would never work'.

These are aspects of economics, the 'dismal science', that are rarely discussed. Here was a distribution system running parallel to, and working better than, the cash economy. Great emphasis has been placed, especially recently, on the wonderful role played by the 'market' – Adam Smith's 'hidden hand' is meant to work magic behind the scenes. Those who suggest interfering with this quasi-divine machination are severely castigated – yet the evidence of the war years points in a rather different direction.

Cash is countable. It is known as 'hard' cash. Yet it is entirely a figment. It is a notion. It is an abstract entity which we believe in, most of the time. Above all, it has no concrete equivalent – it used to be measured against a known weight of uncommon metals, silver and gold. But nowadays these are put to better use elsewhere. The Economist newspaper has fun checking its equivalence to the price of a large hamburger in a bun – not such dismal thinking after all.

No, cash exists only in the imagination. It is but one component of our mental furniture. As such, it comes under the axiom of Truth, Trust and Consent, without which it perishes or becomes so unstable as to be counterproductive, if not actively anti-social, as noted in Part Five.

Cash oils the wheels of human interchange. It enables us to carry out corporately projects and excursions which would simply be non-starters without it. But it cannot do everything. It is supposed to represent value – so many ducats for weeding the field, so many more for building that wall – but it has tighter limits than is usually imagined.

One of the problems we have already touched upon – if you do not feel Lovable, at least you can feel wealthy. Another is that if you have difficulty with social skills, you can show panache by spraying coinage around. And nowadays there are too many ways in which human beings can be violated – monetary coercion occurs far more often than ever it should.

All these factors colour our thinking, they distort the options we appear to have and they savagely limit our inherent ability to build better social stabilities and peace. Just as we need to corral our emotions so that we make them work better for us, so too we need to take a firmer grip on the foundations of our economies, so that they too are more constructive, and assist our overall goals, rather than devastating too many aspirations. If a more benign view of humanity can once prevail, then this should have a material impact on economics.

You cannot buy Truth, you cannot purchase Trust, and Consent given under fiscal duress is void and toxic. Equally, as before you cannot introduce change, unless you can first procure Consent. Much play is made of the 'immorality' of wealth redistribution. Gross discrepancies of income contribute directly to increased social instability (to say nothing of decreased economic performance), from which the rich suffer as much as the poor. Confiscatory taxes to remedy the balance, without Consent infringe the axiomatic rights of the wealthy and thereby risk doing more harm than good. But if ration books could work under conditions of great national stress – there are surely many alternatives to try, if the intent is there.

Buying and Selling

Of course in order to buy something, there has to be something there for sale. During the war there was not enough – so to prevent the rich glutting themselves and the poor starving, the whole community agreed to a planned and regulated economy which brought benefits to all. Perhaps, in our current global economy, we need to do the same again. Imaginative solutions are urgently called for. Certainly nowadays famines occur exclusively as a result of maladministration – this is not to say that they are not real enough, but it focuses more attention on their true origin, and on their permanent remedy. Organizing human relations optimally is not optional, it is vital. The ability to be Sociable is our evolutionary 'advantage', remember. Without it, we risk becoming extinct, bit by bit.

Behind the notional entity that we daily accept as 'cash', there is a deeper significance. Cash is countable, we can hoard it, we can weigh it. It is too easy to credit it with more substance than reality allows. For all it ever is, is a means of exchange. Something is given for something else. The only creatures which ever do this exchanging are other human beings. It has no relevance to anything whatsoever, unless it can enlist human aid; it has no possible use or value unless there is something out there for sale. The only agencies that I have ever heard of who might sell something are human beings.

Now human beings are not countable (in that monetary sense), hoardable or weighable. Human beings partake of the most profound mystery in the entire cosmos, simply by being conscious and alive. Human beings also have values. Indeed they are the only things which do. And these values come from all those rascally emotions which inflict havoc when they get out of hand. So it is doubly damaging to attribute too much of this human-based value to crinkly notes and oily coins.

Public physical health was the major contribution of the Victorians. Sewers took away infectious diseases which decimated both rich and poor alike – from orphans in the streets up to Prince Albert himself. Public libraries were there to expand poor minds as well as rich. And the penny post enabled even the less well-to-do to communicate far and wide.

But our environment, especially our social environment, is constantly changing – there is little benefit in re-fighting yesterday's enemies. The problems in this century are different, and the solutions demand just as much new thinking, new flights of the imagination today as ever they did yesterday. But we have a choice, as always. We can stick with what we know, stay with the strategies we worked out so painfully all those years ago – or we can prepare to discard them and adopt something that might succeed. The choice is still there for us to make, at least it is at the time of writing.

And today the harsh reality is that our main social disease is poverty, even more potent in the damage it does to society than cholera or the other enteric diseases were to the Victorians. We need a Public Health project, as bold and altruistic as theirs, which safely and consensually eliminates poverty. Reform of our other irrational institutions is considered in Part Five.

Maladministration is costly. It causes deaths by famine. It causes unrest in dictatorships or centrally planned economies. But it fractures societies, even when they are ostensibly democratic. It demands a far more stringent perspective on economics in general. Take just one illustration. Monetarism has been much in vogue, though hopefully it is now beginning to wane. For whatever else it is, it is clearly a tax on the poor. If you possess £1000 and interest rates are raised by 1 per cent, your gain is £10. If you own £1,000,000, adding 1 per cent brings £10,000 – rather more than the average weekly wage.

Imperishable Values

Values, especially imperishable values, are certainly available, but, like so many things in this curious life, they are not immediately obvious. Value is essentially in the eye of the beholder, or customer as we generally call her or him. But as we noted, you cannot buy something that is not for sale, and you cannot sell something that has no buyer. So values are certainly there, but perhaps less tangibly than we might wish.

Diamonds, for example, are often thought to be of high value – the bigger the better. But imagine one the size of Asia, but situate on the planet Neptune – its value here is zero. Worse, imagine the same diamond on planet earth – again the value would be zero, and we would change its name to sand. If this is puzzling, remember we are dealing with the most complex entity known to Man or Woman. And if economics ever seems just a touch complex or somewhat infuriatingly incomprehensible – then don't look too far for the cause – these are entirely the characteristics of the human beings whose economic behaviour it purports to describe.

So let's look at values from the other end. If you have a loaf of bread and you wish to share it with another, each of you gets half a loaf. Now if you have an idea, a mental loaf, a nugget of mental sustenance, and you share that – the result is not halved but doubled. In terms of productivity, that is an enviable ratio. It would seem highly rational to exploit it, perhaps through that much neglected device, education.

Of course there are three values which in terms of mental resources are quite invaluable. They pass here under the axiom of Truth, Trust and Consent. Again they are not absolute, they can be polluted and they are in constant need of repair – but when they are in working order the effect on human beings is infinitely preferable to any Aladdin's cave. And again, the more they are shared, and the wider they are disseminated – then the greater the value to us all. Indeed we might all live that bit longer, and all become just a shade Emotionally Healthier.

It is striking how casually Truth, for example, is maltreated. Thatcher, for one, entered the 1979 election declaring publicly that she would never increase VAT – while simultaneously negotiating with the Treasury to double it, which she did. Here is a classic example of devaluing the currency – in this case the verbal currency. This has led to the whole vitally important area of taxation being reviewed in a nonsensical and essentially puerile manner.

If we could think things through more calmly, we might indeed adjust our economic levers towards more imperishable values. What a challenge for economics, and for us all.

What to Expect from Friends and Other Emotional Allies

Allow me to introduce you to the cuckoo duck. This remarkable creature has the shortest childhood development of any higher animal that I know. As its name suggests, the mother duck lays her eggs, not in her own nest, but in that of another species – in the video clip I saw, it was a gull – and never sees hide or feather of it ever again. On hatching, the duckling pushes its way through the wing feathers of its foster mother, who I am sure would express puzzlement, if she could, at the sight of a duckbill on a gull chick. Within hours of leaving its shell, the duckling hops over the side, and swims off into the reeds to feed. No need to bother pushing the other eggs out of the nest like our cuckoo does – there is no sibling rivalry called for, there are no parental favours to covet. In effect, there are no parents.

The cuckoo duckling paddles off and fends for itself within hours of being cooped up inside a tightly packed egg. Here are we, going through up to two decades of struggle and strife being brought up, or bringing up some of the most challenging individuals we ever meet (since they come to know us better than most) – and yet here we have an avian colleague who, immediately on birth, plops over the side and disappears from parental view entirely, whether blood, foster or any other sort of parent whatsoever.

Why do we do the one and they do the other? Do they know something we don't? And, above all, how do they do it? Well, the answer to this last question is, that I do not know. More, I do not know anyone who does. The reason this duckling dispenses with parenting is unknown. Worse than that – no one knows, and indeed no one will or can ever know. We have here an 'indelible ignorance'. This might not be such a popular notion – we do like to know as much as we can, so if we come across an unknowability then we feel uncomfortable. But this is just such a one – it is quite unknowable to human beings why cuckoo ducklings turn their back on parenting.

There are too many reasons to go into here as to why this ignorance is indelible. But let us take just one. We will never know why this duckling needs no parenting, because ducks were laying eggs long before we arrived. We were not around when they first started doing it, so there are one or two factors we cannot know. Suppose we call on our common human heritage – we can read items from perhaps 10,000 years ago – but there are few comments in the written record relating to why ducks, or indeed chickens, lay eggs.

And if we go further back, we come to an interesting time, some 75,000 years ago, when the human species was all but wiped out. The Sumatra Super-Volcano, similar to the one currently pending under Yellowstone National Park, blew all us humans away, apart from a residual 1000 or so. So any common heritage would date back to that point, when every member of the human race could know every other – an interesting thought. When the next one blows – will the remaining 1000 do as well?

We are uncomfortable with ignorance, for an excellent reason – if we don't know certain vital facts, then, depending on quite how vital they are – our very survival is at risk. And the nature of knowledge, I should say the uncomfortable nature of knowledge, is that it is inherently imperfect. There are no absolutes, there are too many antecedents, there is simply too much going on for us to 'know' with anything approaching 100 per cent certainty, a point taken further in Part Five.

So we are back in tiger country – we cannot be everywhere, so we need friends and other emotional allies. Without them, we are lost in ignorance, potentially dangerous ignorance. With them, we have a chance. The trouble is we need to find out if they are telling the Truth, and whether we can Trust them when they do. Most of us are an awkward lot, still struggling to understand what happened when we left the nest, and generally far too preoccupied with the unhappy experiences we have had, the miserable training we have received, to open ourselves too warmly to our neighbours.

But that's the way out, the way forwards. In fact, it is the only way. That is, if you want a more secure and peaceful life – and one in which your emotions stop telling you that disaster is upon you and allow you to enjoy more of the days you have left. If you cannot build better social networks and find more trustworthy emotional allies – then we all lose.

Why Should You Care?

The cuckoo duck intrigues me. I would like to conclude that it never has a single neurosis, panic attack or one instant irrational emotion in its entire life. If irrational emotions arise through misperceiving childhood experiences or mistaking parenting – then if it doesn't have either of these, perhaps it doesn't have any of the ill-fated consequences which so plague us.

Let us suppose, for argument's sake, that the duckling in question has a somewhat limited intellectual life. It must recognize and distinguish edible grubs and other items from inedible ones, though we have not the slightest idea how it ever acquired this knowledge. It begs the question to say that all ducklings who couldn't tell the difference died out from food poisoning – whatever else life might be, and evolution with it, it is vastly more sophisticated and indeed successful than random pot shots in every direction. No, somehow our duckling was programmed to know.

But I think it is safe to assume that whereas its mind may be full of information about what to do if a hawk flies over, where to look for food, how to mate and indeed how to find another gullible gull's nest – none of which it has ever been taught – its mental equipment is less extensive than our own. Indeed it would seem entirely appropriate that the reason we have large brains, and larger minds to go with them, relates entirely to our Sociable lifestyle. Wales, dolphins and all higher animals which go around in pods or groups all invariably have enormous cerebral capacities, to cope with the vagaries of 'other people'.

Now the larger the brain, the wider the mind, and the vastly more extensive the mental furniture – how can we cope? Well, one way that is no longer viable is to try and know everything, to be self-sufficient in facts and knowledge. This was always rather a tall order – since Einstein and others, and especially the philosopher David Hume, it has become quite impossible. It follows that we have such large and unwieldy minds that we cannot manage them on our own. We cannot patrol them adequately, we cannot vouch for their validity at all times – we have outgrown our capacity to own a mental world without adequate social assistance.

There may be fewer tigers around the street corner these days, but there are plenty of other hazards. If you listen to some of my more handicapped customers, the world is merely a string of calamities loosely cobbled together, each waiting to sink you, without further trace.

And what is the remedy against these impending disasters? What can we sensibly do to avert them, or at least reduce them to manageable proportions?   Well, the first requirement is to become more confident, to become mentally healthier and stronger – and the only possible way to do that is with allies.

Here is the curious thing about Sociable human beings – the person opposite you can benefit as much, if not more, from social contact with you, as you with them. If you are churlish, cold and cut yourself off, if you contribute to macerating your social contacts on a regular basis – then your companions, your daily contacts, suffer. And so do you.

You may suppose that everyone else out there is just smug – they are sitting pretty, thank you very much, and they need no truck with you. You may have been taught this. You may believe it more certainly than anything else – but if you can inch your eye open a touch wider than that, and see yourself through others' eyes, the answer to the question why you or they should care will become obvious. And when you see it, it might well surprise you.

I can't get over this duck. All my working life I have been struggling to understand just what it was in our childhood training that so disabled us emotionally. To uncover what it was that so precisely pickled us for coping realistically with the most important emotional events and opportunities that come at us in adult life. And here we have a warm-blooded creature which is clearly still thriving – and yet it does none of the things that we find so debilitating – it has no inadequate parenting – it has none. Parenting does not keep it alive as an infant – it fends for itself from day one. So, on this definition, it cannot become insane. It cannot develop such a mismatch between its mental picture of the world and the reality outside – such that it ceases to function sensibly. Would it be entirely petulant of me to suppose it didn't have much of a mind to begin with?

As a species our evolutionary choice has been to go the social route. We ducked out of the speed stakes and threw in our lot with the socials. Well, socializing is not easy. It demands we learn any number of complex skills. Speech, for example, doesn't come naturally. Even now we have no reliable rules of grammar – and when we have, we keep a-changing them. Humans delight in neologizings and other plays on words which intrigue and sometimes illuminate.

So by going down the social evolutionary route, to survive we have to make it work. Where it does not, we starve in famines and elsewhere. But there is a cost to this route. If, for whatever reason, we fail to pick up enough during our extensive childhood training, then our socializing will be deficient. And if our socializing is deficient, then our health, especially our mental health, is jeopardized.

It may surprise you to find these deeper questions of evolution being considered alongside possible pathways to Emotional Health. But the first axiom states that Truth is of the essence. And Truth in this context implies being ever more realistic. If we are less, then our chances of adapting to our environment are diminished if not abolished.

So the Truth is that you do need to care about what friends and other emotional allies are for, and what we should do about seeking or shunning them. You need other human beings out there who can bolster your supplies of Truth, Trust and Consent, who can help you past the vicissitudes that life has a habit of throwing up at us all.

If this is already easy for you, then it will be obvious and apparent without any need for argument. But if it is less so, then we need to draw upon all manner of lines of reasoning to try and prise open your limited social perceptions. The challenge for you is to confirm or refute the axiom that, underneath everything, we all wish to be Lovable, Sociable and Non-violent. The evidence against is extensive, widely circulated and comes with excellent credentials. It is, in my view, wrong.

When I started this book last month, I never dreamt I would be appealing to a duck to help me out. I would never have believed that I would bring myself to say something along the lines of – if only we can become more like the cuckoo duckling, it might help us all. What a thing for an advanced primate to say about an inferior avian, what a comedown. But that is one of the intriguing things about life – you never can tell – and when you are emotionally confident, this is an imperishable source of delight.

What Neighbours Are for – Building Social Support Networks

You are sitting in the group. It is unlike any group you have been in before. There are an assortment of different people – some with similar problems to yours, some with quite a different approach to life. The group is sitting all in a circle, in a room on the fifth floor of a tall hospital building – with extensive if grimy views out over the city. The chairs are not uniform, there are rather battered tables about, in fact the whole room could do with a good lick of paint – but so tight is the department for space that we are lucky to have it. The group starts as usual, with a 'go-round' – each is asked in turn what has happened to them in the last week, what they thought about the last group and whether it helped or not.

On this occasion we have a newcomer. She sits down, nearest the door. She is clearly nervous, almost literally on the edge of her chair, ready to spring up at any moment and bolt. The go-round starts in a leisurely fashion. It starts with those nearest my left hand, and will take some time to reach our new friend. I thought this might help her settle down and give her a flavour of the group, before being called on to say anything.

The go-round is flowing smoothly. These are settled members of the group. They know what we are about and they are confident that what they have to say is of value, is going to be listened to and will be likely to help other members of the group. They are startled, however, when, in the midst of this preamble, the newcomer leaps to her feet and interrupts the conversation. 'I have to go now,', she says matter of factly but with great conviction, 'I have a dental appointment that I do not want to be late for.'. And she starts to make for the door.

Instantly, and quite unexpectedly from my point of view, most of the existing members of the group stop what they are doing and focus entirely upon her. Without a second thought they reach out to her verbally. 'No,' they say. 'Stay. This will help you. We have problems just like yours, and this is the place to get help for them.'

How do they know? She hasn't opened her mouth. I have seen her on a number of occasions earlier, to discuss her underlying 'frozen terrors', and to get her used to me, so that I can support her and encourage her to come to the group. But they know nothing of her. This is the first time they have set eyes on her, and they know only her first name. They know nothing about who she is, where she is from or, as it seemed to me, what could possibly be wrong with her.

In the event, for all my careful preparation, I am quite useless in helping decide the question as to whether she stays or goes. I don't say anything. For one thing, it is axiomatic with me that she attends by Consent or not at all. Painful things are discussed and disclosed here, so attendance is strictly on a wish-to-stay basis. So, however valuable I think it may be for her, or indeed for any of the others – this carries no weight whatsoever in whether or not the individual decides to stay in the group.

I have inside knowledge, and my advice to her is to stay – yet this counts for nothing. She is up and ready for off. But there is something in the directness of her fellow group members' pleas, there is a powerful sense of comradeship, or friendship, of being a supportive neighbour. And she pauses. Not for me, but for them. These people, she recognizes, have intimate knowledge of what is going on inside her – they are inviting her to Trust them, to join them. And she does.

You might have thought this was my group, that I was in charge of it, that I said who came and went, and what happened in it. You might have thought I was the governor of it, and if I didn't like it, it would not happen. But the Truth is that the group really was 'owned' by its members. It had taken on a life of its own – and the members of the group knew this. They relished it. It was their group, and they wanted to use it to help this complete stranger, with her odd ways and awkward habits. She could be very abrupt at times, as she was when she peremptorily declared that it was not for her, that she had suddenly rediscovered a dental appointment to use as her infallible escape hatch.

I came to think of these groups as if they were some kind of furnace. They took some time to ignite, but once alight they burned up all the dross that was standing in the way of its members being Lovable, Sociable and Non-violent – and the tools it put into practice were Truth, Trust and Consent.

I suppose one of the things that I did do when establishing this, and other group sessions, was to insist at the beginning that we were all equal, that we were all adults and that we all wanted to be more confident, more autonomous, with better self-esteem and better control of the awesome emotions which had so bewildered us. The essential switch is to move from me doing it all to trusting that the group members want to do it for themselves. Once the furnace is alight, the glow is astonishing, almost miraculous. But what it does is reveal, often for the first time to those sitting there, that human beings can be, and want to be, benign. We are, as this experience proves, social animals.

I have learnt enormous quantities about emotions from groups. Indeed the first that I attended in 1963 opened my eyes to a whole new perspective on humanity (to say nothing of a new perspective into myself). It was a little humiliating to begin with, but so gratifying and so helpful in setting the emotions into their proper context – something my previous training had succeeded entirely in getting wrong.

The emotions I discovered in myself in 1963 were not the deepest, nor the most sinister. But they were a start. I then began to take them seriously – something I have done ever since. I would like to record my debt to Dr Denis Martin, then Superintendent of Claybury Hospital in Essex – a remarkable man, powerful, knowledgeable, but humble, who laid the foundation stones for the rest of my emotional expeditions.

But these groups tell a deeper story. All you need is a group of human beings – in those I have organized these are generally the less successful individuals amongst us, with negative social skills as described earlier. You then add to this group a hefty dose of reassurance – no one is going to push them where they do not wish to go. You lay the ground rules and watch it take off. Of course, the only ground rules that matter are axiomatic – Truth, Trust and Consent. These may be easy to write down, they may trip off the tongue without difficulty – but putting them into practice is often more of a challenge.

But this is where my confidence comes from – that underneath everyone of us is the wish, and indeed the need, to be Lovable, Sociable and Non-violent. I even managed some sort of group in Parkhurst Prison. The officers did not want one, declaring that groups were something they did not have on that Special Unit. They set me up in the wrong room, at the wrong time, and watched to see me stumble. They had not counted on the persistence of the prisoners – one of whom said, 'You want a group – I'll get you one.' He set about 'volunteering' all those who answered his three-line whip, to come and sit and talk on a regular basis. It was an educative experience, and assisted more than one extremely damaged individual in ways which I do not believe any other approach could have done.

So this is what real neighbours are like. This is where they come from. This is what neighbours are for. We all need neighbours to help us carry the overwhelming burden of our overgrown minds – and we need them to reassure us that we are a Sociable species, who thrive on Trust and Consent. If you do not think you are your brother or sister's keeper – who is? And who is there to look after you?

Keeping your brother or your sister is thus an entirely profitable exercise, provided it is done democratically and exclusively with Consent. The other proviso, which gives 'keeping others' a bad name, is, of course, parenting. If you go parenting anyone other than an infant, then you need your mind examining, to say nothing of your emotions.

But social support networks are remarkable things. They are hard to imagine if you've never had one. And they are hard to establish in today's generally undemocratic and anti-social society. But they are quite essential.

If we want a more Emotionally Healthy society, which for our security and well-being we certainly should – then we need to institute those social structures which allow these latent sociabilities to emerge.

It does not do to overlook the obstacles. The most recent group that I established was in a maximum security hospital. I was raucously assured by my psychiatric colleagues that the patients in the Personality Disorder Unit were untreatable – they would not benefit from treatment, they could not benefit from it. They were also 'treatment-resistant' – they would do anything to avoid treatment. From the sound of it, they were a thoroughly bad lot. The notion that they could in any way be   Lovable or Sociable was too laughable to even give breath to. I assured such as wanted to listen that I only proceeded with Consent – that is, no one was to attend who did not do so voluntarily – which, of course, confirmed their professional view that what I proposed was a complete non-starter.

So naturally I started anyway. How far can you get if you let other people's prejudices bar your way?   As it happened, it was those prejudices which saw me off the premises pretty promptly – but not before I had proved my point, indeed it was probably precisely because I had proved my point.

I chose my first ward. I gave my spiel to the assembled 'ward community meeting'. I told them what I wanted to do, and that I would turn up every Monday and Thursday on the dot of 11 o'clock. On the first Monday, eight showed, and then ever after six insisted on coming, until the consultant psychiatrists stood at the doorway to the group, forbidding them entry.

Just take a moment to consider who these people are – they are the criminally insane. Notorious serial killers were in a neighbouring ward. Yet they came, sat down and talked. One of them said if the notion of Truth, Trust and Consent meant anything, then he didn't Consent to members of staff sitting in the group. So we compromised. Then he revealed something from his past that even he did not know – something which thoroughly explained his crime, which was appalling, and explained how to undo the turmoil in his head that had led up to it, which was equally appalling.

His friend, sitting next to him, expressed astonishment. He said he had known this man for ten years, having been in that hospital with him for that long, and had never heard him describe the experience he had just spoken of. The reason for this is that it represented a 'frozen terror' – it had, up to that point, been too terrifying for him to contemplate, let alone recite in open company.

If social support networks can be set up, if only briefly, in the environment most hostile to them, and with the least likely candidates for them – then there is nowhere on earth that they cannot be established. And when they are, their primary function is to burn away the dross we all accumulate in our prolonged emotional development during our unusually long childhood.

Prejudice is destructive. If it closes our eyes to our true underlying nature, then no wonder we have trouble trusting each other. But if we can once learn to reverse this unhappy process, we can burn up all such misperceptions in a fiery furnace, and thereby improve our Emotional Health beyond recognition.

We All Need Kith and Kin

Charles Darwin was remarkable. When you consider the prejudices in favour of an authoritarian God who had created everything in a week – then Darwin's achievements were astonishing – no wonder he took so long to come to publication. Even today there are those who give his reasoning short shrift. I wonder how they would react to the knowledge that today there is, as I mentioned earlier, below

Yellowstone National Park, a humungous quantity of lava which even as we speak, is inching its way upwards, having nowhere else to go, prior to blasting miles into the sky and shutting out the sun for a decade or two. We have no defence against this. Perhaps, if we got together early enough, we might make some provision – but we'll make none at all if we continue to believe that other members of our own species are the ones to attack since they are seen as our enemy. Sociability is our only possible remedy against extinction.

Darwin could only take the argument so far. There are stages he preferred not to go to, steps he preferred not to take. For one thing he did not, as we shall in Part Five, give due priority to intent. And for another, he emphasized the survival of the fittest against other members of the same species. This is how he accounted for the peacock's tail and the duck's webbed feet – a remarkable explanatory achievement in itself. But what he did not emphasize enough was the survival of living organisms against the environment.

Living processes combat the Second Law of Thermodynamics, which in abbreviated form says everything cools. Entropy, the degree of disorganization, tends always to increase in every physical system you can name – your desk always tends to get untidier, your buildings, whether bricks and mortar or otherwise, always tend to become crumblier. Disorganization forever tends to increase – except in living organisms.

Life organizes. Don't ask me how it does it, or what it uses to defy this supposedly immutable inexorable law of physics – but it does, else you and I would not be here. For one thing we would have cooled off, fatally, the minute we left our parents' warmth. For another, our bodies would have worn out quicker than any mechanical device we daily use. Tyres wear out on cars, paint blisters off woodwork – yet even when we cut ourselves, we heal, the damage is repaired. Our tissues organize themselves so that they are better than new.

How?   Why? Is this really True?   These are questions I prefer to leave to you.

It was in 1960, while examining this facility for resisting disintegration, which no inanimate process possesses, that the true significance of 'adapt and survive' shone through. Living organisms, as Darwin pointed out, have the ability to adapt, they have the ability to respond to adverse changes in their environment. We've seen that they cannot do this without breaching the Second Law of Thermodynamics, as indicated – but if we are wise, we do not hold that against them.

Suppose we granted living organisms, ourselves included, the ability to respond. Suppose further that we merged these two terms to give us a 'responding-ability' – it is only a small jump to contract this to 'responsibility'. Here is a vital basis for the key ethical concept. If you exercise your responding-ability, your responsibility, then you will take into account not only the changes you need to adapt to in your surroundings, but also the impact you have on those around you. If you fail in this, it will not be a divine ordinance that will strike you down with a thunderbolt – no, it will be just one further notch cut in your non-survivability index.

So here is another indication that 'sociability' pays. The less Sociable you are, the less you respond to the society around you, whether micro- or macro-, then to that degree you are impairing your ability to adapt, and thence your ability to survive.

Why Poverty Matters

Bad news travels. Atrocities matter, so you will tend to hear, and nowadays tend to see, on the news media far more inhumanity than its opposite. Your emotions are there to warn you about disasters, so as to help you avoid them – there is therefore a never-ending thirst for bad news. But the only

176   *Why Poverty Matters*

remedy for everyday problems of whatever level, whether disastrous or otherwise, is to seek mutual emotional support from those around us we Trust.

And just as the more you share a mental loaf, the bigger it grows – so with our social support – the wider the better.

But today we live in a narrow society. So narrow that the wealthy shut themselves away in ghettos, hoarding their material wealth as they squander their social and emotional treasure.

The index ratio between the wealthiest and the poorest grows. There is no consensus that it should not. There is substantial evidence that nations in which this index becomes narrower are both more productive and less unstable. But this runs counter to what we have so deeply learned in our difficult childhoods. Fear of deprivation runs deep, and fear being what it is, this tends to colour our perceptions, invariably for the worse. So, as with all irrationality, any evidence to the contrary is blinked at, and counts for little.

The savage irony is that only a little of our vast excess of wealth would transform the situation in a twinkling. In the world today there are 400 billionaires and five million millionaires, with 69 new millionaires being added every day. Just as it takes remarkably little from any one of us adults to calm the volcanic eruptions of a newborn babe– so, relatively speaking, we could fund an abolition of global poverty without even feeling the pinch.

But what we do need is clarity of vision. We need to see that other members of our own species are valuable in themselves. They are not squabbling for crumbs off our table that we can ill afford to let them have, they are not pestering us for vital supplies which would threaten our survival if we let them have them. They are not asking us to work, while they laze about. No, what they need we could easily deliver

– and the effect on them, and thereby on us, would be little short of miraculous.

How many billions have we spent on devising delivery systems for toxic thermonuclear radiation products?   Why not spend a fraction of this on delivery systems of washing machines and other white goods, desalination plants, solar panels, computers and other necessities?   Why not devise systems which assist those of our fellows who currently beg, who are currently deeply mired in inescapable poverty?   In the Victorian era everyone from royalty downwards benefited from public sewerage – so too, in the present day, we would all benefit from an ending of this gross disease of poverty. Poverty poisons all societies, so we need to enskill the pauper and buy her product.

It shouldn't require a medical or a criminological argument to bolster the need to be Sociable as a matter of course. But it's there if you need it. Tuberculosis thrives amid squalor – yet, even before antibiotics, we were defeating TB, by improving living conditions. The TB sanatoria, using simple measures of nutrition and comfort, led to early successes. The graph of TB infection was falling just before streptomycin joined the fight. And as TB becomes steadily more drug-resistant, then these older remedies will again become our only medical defence.

And violence is a similar social disease. Near Yale University in the late 1980s child physical abuse was abolished by the provision of support for stressed families – and there is nothing more stressful than poverty. It is clear that poverty is a disease – it inflicts so much damage in both the short term and the long term, shortens lives and terminates hope. Perhaps calling it a disease may help attract the necessary remedies to eradicate it.

My Benign Thread

What has surprised me, over the past 40 years, is the way in which all the complex threads inherent in complicated living human organisms have steadily come closer together, at least it seems to me they have. Thus by being pragmatic, we are also being responsible – there is no other more reliable way through the pressing problems which surround us. Being responsible works. It led me to the notion that a parent's responsibility ends as the threshold of adulthood is passed – quite a novelty at the time, especially given my own (dependent) emotional status.

Then there was the significance of Human Rights. I was taught as a medical student that only the fool operated in the absence of a signed Consent form. Somehow Consent had crept into medical practice. It has crept out again, at least as far as psychiatry is currently being taught. But this is an issue for the next chapters.

More recently, the notion of intent has come to the fore. It has always been there in the practice of law, but it has never been there in the practice of science. Determinism is the order of the day – for reasons which have more to do with our own inability to think clearly, and our morbid resistance towards ignorance, than with the raw objective evidence that stares at us daily from our soup bowl or kitchen sink.

Consent, which is a close cousin of intent, is a mighty curious item. When I first heard that the duty of the United States Congress to the President was to 'advise and consent', I thought this was a very queer fish. But, as usual, the sages of the past knew more. Normally, especially in our current coercive society, those who give Consent are seen as displaying a weakness, which, in the Hollywood Syndrome, is generally portrayed as a fatal weakness. It turns out that we cannot have a stable society without it.

Consent means that you have been able to engage the intent of the other person. This represents a dynamic support, it ensures that the other individual will assert their inherent facility of responding and adapting to support your joint project. Nothing is then surer. You may fail, you may have to readapt, redeploy and rearrange the whole caboodle – but at least you are in business, you have a viable proposition. Compare this with a coercive project which lasts only as long as you can keep your charges in view and can maintain sufficient force to overwhelm them. Coercion provokes resistance in its very inception – and resistance is being operated and driven by sentient human beings, with a creativity or two up their sleeve – so beware.

The more Consent there is, the safer and more secure we can all be. In the past governments operated by the Consent of landowners and of the wealthy in general. The poor were disenfranchised. The rich bought peerages and other political insurances, much as they do today. Then it was noticed that some of the population were not of the male gender, so, ever so reluctantly, they too were included in the process of democratic government.

In England since the Norman Conquest, we have been governed by the rich and powerful. Recently the House of Lords, supposedly part of our democratic government, has been part-reformed – instead of being chosen by the King or the Prime Minister – these legislators are next to be chosen by those appointed by the latter rather than by the Consent of those being legislated upon.

Why not enlist economics again?   Commerce thrives when the customers' views are heard. Wouldn't governments do the same?   Consumer choice has radically improved consumer services. Isn't it time the same was applied to our administrations – bearing in mind the unhappy consequences of maladministration, of which we now suffer a bundle.

Poverty effectively disenfranchises whole swathes of the electorate, especially in the USA. Why not devise an economic system which empowers them financially? Then we would begin to get the political stability that we deserve. Poverty is not only medically and judicially unsound, it is also politically disastrous. It stands as a constant rebuke against our maladministrations.

But reverse it by policy, and, just as consumer choice transforms commerce – so we would all benefit by the views of the poor being expressed not only electorally, but via the cash economy.

Is it really beyond our wit to devise a means of extending to the poor a financial lever to express their intents, so we can take them into account in governing our ship of state, and so guide it more successfully into safer waters?

There is a golden thread which links our individual emotional needs with our remarkable human ability and extends this from the individual to the social level. When our societies and our social institutions are more humanely organized, as discussed further in Part Five, our imperishable values can be immeasurably uplifted.

Part Four –
Poisonous
Red
Herrings

Debunking Current 'Solutions'
For Emotional Distress

Emotional Health

Part Four – Poisonous Red Herrings

11 Is Psychiatry Bankrupt?

The Five Points • Does Our Choice Really Matter? • The Impact of 'Intent' • The Mind Is Greater than the Brain • Computers Can't Think • There's a Gene for It – So What? • Born Evil or Born Lovable?

You are sitting across the desk from your work's psychiatrist. He doesn't seem too pleased. He has been shuffling through his papers for a while now and making little progress. You repeat your request – 'I want a Medical Tribunal to review my dismissal.' He grunts. You get the feeling that he may not be too kindly disposed towards you and your problem. So you explain yet again – 'I was on the fast-track promotion scheme for young managers. I was good. I was doing well, then I had this aberration. I'm better now, and I want to be reinstated – there was a medical cause for my actions, and it's all over.'

He glances up. Your request is slowly dying of neglect. He mutters something inconclusive, which doesn't help. You become exasperated – so eventually you point to a report you can see lying on the desk. 'Look at that report from Dr Johnson – it explains everything that happened to me, and why I am now better.' This seems to hit a nerve. He becomes animated. He acknowledges the report but with obvious reluctance. Choosing his words carefully, he says, 'Dr Johnson's report is pure speculation'.

You are aghast. This is the last thing you expected to hear. 'But,' you splutter, 'it cured me.' You came here in good faith, you knew that there had been difficulties, you had behaved erratically – but you now knew why, and expected your doctor to read the report which explained what had gone wrong and why it was not going to go wrong again. You expected him to be as interested in the positive outcome as you had been. He wasn't.

Here was a medical problem – you suffered from it, your work went haywire – you discussed your family problems, your grieving and your fears – and now you see it all entirely clearly, it will not happen again. And you want this doctor to take note. He does not. He is working to one agenda, you are working to another. The evidence you give him that you are now emotionally fit and strong does not even register. He does not believe you are any different now than you were. Your claim to be cured does not even flicker across his mind – what is going on with this profession?

You present the argument, you have the evidence to prove your case – but it doesn't make any difference at all – the doctor hardly looks up from the paperwork. Needless to say, a medical tribunal is not granted.

If this was an isolated incident it would count for little. But if it was repeated, incessantly, throughout the land – then there would be serious issues at stake. What could you do with a branch of the medical profession which simply refuses, as this work's psychiatrist did, to look at the clinical evidence before its very eyes?   If psychiatry ever gave up learning – then the end result would be parlous. Here indeed would be evidence to support the notion that psychiatry is bankrupt.

The Five Points

There are five points in which psychiatry currently misses the boat. They are –

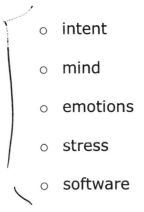

- o intent
- o mind
- o emotions
- o stress
- o software

Now, if one or other of these were a little askew, then perhaps the whole ship might glide onwards a little less speedily. But if all five are out of order, then psychiatry is in real trouble. Should psychiatrists be trained to go by the book rather than by what they see in front of them, then correction by clinical experience will tend to be slow. And, as in many professions, promotion is by word of mouth – those hoping to progress have to be careful what they say.

It is not surprising that psychiatry struggles with the five problems listed. The first item – intent – is not, as we have mentioned, an easy fish to land. It is decidedly wrigglesome – and even as you believe you are getting closer to an understanding of it, it flips off down the bank and back into the deeps. But if it makes the difference between guilt and innocence in a case of law, then we need to pay it due attention – and if it makes the difference between lunacy and sanity in psychiatry, then to ignore it could prove most unhealthy. Could this be why many current psychiatric problems are labelled 'not mentally ill' or 'untreatable'?

Not only is intent difficult to define, or even to describe very clearly – it also runs rings round any permanent knowledge. You cannot by definition, know something in advance, if the intentions are not clear beforehand. Suppose you decided that all humans would go for more money every time there was a choice – and you built a society on that basis. What would happen if they changed their minds?   What would happen to your model, to your way of thinking, if each individual sometimes did and sometimes did not follow this rule?

There is a serious risk that you would be tempted to say that when they showed intent, that they were out of step – that what really mattered was the knowledge base, and anything that suggested we could not know absolutely what was happening should be suppressed or ignored.

Intent flourishes in the practice of law – when you picked up that spade, did you intend to dig or to kill?   Lawyers do not blush when they ask this question, they do not feel foolish, or risk being drummed out of work. No, on the contrary, they would be negligent if they ignored the issue. In psychiatry, and in the academic sciences, intent does not exist, it is something that they simply do not want to know. Which is sad, since without it you cannot be sane.

You can either have intent, the ability to make choices, the option of taking decisions – or you can live in an fully deterministic 'clockwork' universe. To preserve the illusion of the latter, academic science, and psychiatry with it, has preferred to suppose that we are all machines, like 'mindless unfeeling robots' – at least that way there is a glimmer of hope that eventually we should be able to 'know' all about us. This obsessive retention of deterministic biology is a face-saving device to preserve theoretical models intact. A costly preservation – since it cripples everything else.

Suppose you went to a mechanic and explained that your car was not really performing up to scratch. How would you react if she opened your boot and dumped in a sack of coal?   This was because she believed in steam power – always had, always will – and if you needed more oomph, then there was nothing like a dose of coal to improve matters. She believed in it so strongly that she felt no need to explain anything to you.

If you pointed out that this was all rather nineteenth century, that nowadays we used internal-combustion engines and were shortly moving on to fuel cells – you would expect your protestations to make some impact and elicit an intervention that made just a little more sense to you. But no, your remarks are dismissed as pure speculation.

It seems likely that you would exercise your choice, deploy your intention and not revisit the steam-engine enthusiast. But if the whole of the Car Mechanics Training Authorities were steeped in steam engine techniques and other mechanistic ideologies – you might have some difficulty in finding an alternative.

Dumping coal in the boot to make the car work better is obviously ludicrous. But, sadly, it is not more so than insisting that it is your brain cells which are out of order, rather than grief over death of your loved one. It is no more preposterous than denying, at every turn, that what you want, what you intend, what you chose – matters.

But that's the problem – the mentally ill have few rights, and receive little respect. They regard themselves as pathetic, weak and inherently stupid – and too many find it all too easy to agree with them on this point. So if the profession charged with assisting them trains all its members to think in a mechanistic manner, to ignore what the emotions get up to, to wince every time the word 'mind' is mentioned, and to talk of consciousness only when pressed – then the result is dire. It is then entirely feasible to accuse psychiatry of regarding human beings as mindless unfeeling robots and of marching ever more firmly towards bankruptcy.

There are psychiatrists who have known these problems for years. They achieve their results by abandoning the rigidities of the current established view. Sadly, I met few in positions of any power, when trying to work as a psychiatric consultant.

Does Our Choice Really Matter?

When I was young we invented a phrase to cover an eventuality which seemed to occur with disturbing regularity. When one of us knocked something over, there were two possible outcomes. One, we were reprimanded and told not to do it again; or two, we escaped that fate, because it was obviously an accident. Naturally enough, when you are exploring how the world works, especially one in the nursery – you test things out. It follows that we would always attempt to fit more of our misdemeanours into the second category rather than the first.

So when we complained noisily that so and so hit me – we came to know that there were in principle two outcomes – one, they should not have done it, or two – it was only an accident. But our noses being closer to the ground, we could easily detect those occasions when the second party had successfully disguised their assault on our person as an accident, knowing all the while that there had indeed been malice aforethought. We invented the phrase 'accidentally on purpose' to cover those situations where a good telling-off was clearly called for in our favour, but the culprit had escaped due to unusual social skills.

The phrase covered a practical situation. It sounds self-contradictory – in logic an event is either accidental, that is, without known cause or intentional causation – or it is purposeful, in which case we intended it. 'Accidentally on purpose' should therefore be a non-starter. But reality is invariably more complex than the words we use to describe it. As I look back now, it seems entirely reasonable that we should label those events in this way. How else would you distinguish occasions where we could see that deliberate intent had been deployed, generally against us – but that the cloak of 'accident' had been deftly draped over it, so as to deflect parental disapproval.

Now, some 60 years later, similar verbal conundrums still apply, though the consequences are rather heavier. Indeed this nursery nomenclature stands up pretty well against some of the nonsenses that prevail today. Intent is undeniably a challenge. If you endorse it, as I do, then the task of saying what it is, is daunting.

The big question is – can you mean anything at all? When you intend something or other – is that a real choice you have? Or are you fooling yourself?

And here there are echoes of the basics of emotions we discussed in Part One. Here your view of yourself inevitably colours the picture. It reminds us that a 'wholistic' approach is the only practicable one. As with emotions earlier, there is never an intent, or a meaning or a significance on its own – it always comes with a living human being. You cannot have the one without the other. It may seem that you can, and the connection between the two may appear distant, tangled or entirely tenuous – but at root, which is the only way to get any sense out of it – there is a living human being, either intending one thing or not intending another.

Further, the Truth of the situation needs to be established. Is it more true to say that we have intentions, a measure of choice, an element of free will? Or is it truer to say that we are cogs in a vast cosmic clock, where, whatever we say, do or mean, we are but as grains of sand on the seashore, being swept hither and thither, as the tide washes over us?

These are not idle questions. Matters of enormous moment hang upon their resolution. If I have difficulty saying what I mean by intent – then this is as chicken feed compared to those who deny that intent has any validity. For make no mistake about it – we are not different creatures when we find ourselves in the supermarket, or in the laboratory, the polling booth or in the psychiatric ward. If we have choices, and are capable of exercising our choice in the market-place, then we are surely entitled to the same facility for choosing, in our minds.

If you live in a 'clockwork' universe, then obviously you have no choice but to believe that we have no choice either. But to maintain this position, as whole rafts of academic scientists struggle to do – you have to shut your eyes to virtually all human activities, certainly all that have any interest.

It is not easy to say what intent is. It is also hard to live with systems and models and theoretical constructs which award to the smallest cog a freedom to do what it likes on occasion. This is worse than herding cats – and for precisely the same reason – you never know what they will get up to next. They may not even have decided yet. The last way to control them is to decide that they always do exactly what they have done before, or have been caused to do, or, more sharply – what they have been programmed to do. In this way, at least you can pretend to a consistency, a reliability which simply isn't there in practice. It's simply not True.

The issues at stake are huge. It has taken us some millennia to acquire a system of administration we call democratic. The key point of this is that from time to time we get to chose. If you really believe that choosing anything, anything at all, is a mere figment of our imagination – then you must, in all logic and consistency, kiss democracy goodbye. Our democratic institutions are cumbersome, they crumble, they are all too easily corrupted by the rich and powerful, which is exactly whom they should protect us against. Indeed, as I believe Winston Churchill said, democracy is a most unsatisfactory form of government, until you look at the alternatives.

In fact when the parlous state of human knowledge is more widely known, it will come to be seen as obvious that the democratic approach is the only one which has the remotest chance of edging us forwards, rather than backwards into the

Dark Ages. This even applies to such scientific basics as whether we have intent or not.

I would be perfectly happy to put it to the vote – because the simple act of so doing confirms that those taking part believe they have a choice in the matter – which is the prime consideration in the first place.

The Impact of 'Intent'

The current model that psychiatrists are now taught, and which academic scientists also believe, is that we do not have any choice. Whatever we may say, however we may flail about in the wind – we are creatures of a 'clockwork' system that has us in its grip and will spew us out along predetermined lines. In this curious view, it is our sole task to find out what those lines are, so that we can soundly predict the future. If chance nudges our predictions off course, that is something that we have to put up with, and can to some degree make allowances for. But if our results are intentionally altered, or deliberately twisted in a different direction – then this is seen as beyond the pale.

So if you were to go to your work's psychiatrist and ask for a review of your medical case on the grounds that you now see where your emotions had led your astray, and you can therefore confidently assure him or her that you will now be able to deliver on your good intentions – stand by. Do not assume that he or she will agree that you have any choice in the matter. Do not presume that, because it is obvious to you, it will be obvious to him or her, that your intentions make all the difference. Depending precisely on how far the psychiatrist's confidence allows him or her to deviate from the established pattern, he or she will allow or disallow you any control over your state of mind.

This is the crux of the deterministic viewpoint, this is where determinism and human reality cross over and meet. If our dangerous prisoners are bound by their genes to behave the way they do, why bother to talk to them?   If our anorexic customers are determined not to eat – then this is pre-determined, and we must label them untreatable, incurable. Take this too far and 'untreatability' is no longer arguable, it is inevitable.

This therapeutic condemnation does not arise from the particular circumstances of that individual – it arises out of a view of the human condition in general. If you really believe that we none of us have any choice in the matter, any matter – then it is this, rather than any failure to understand the causative factors in a mental disease, which prejudges the therapeutic gloom.

But I would have thought that one anorexic whose intentions change, one 'incurable psychopath' who elects to be Non-violent, one aberrant young manager who sees what went wrong and determines not to let it happen again – if any one of these events occurs, then it is time to rethink the basic mechanistic view of human nature. Intent may be difficult to handle, but it works, and makes a crucial difference, so it behoves us to make whatever provision for it we can.

The Mind Is Greater than the Brain

If the iridescent notion of intent seems to have slipped, with comparative ease, from the grasp of today's psychiatric profession – it will surely come as something of a shock to find that the mind has suffered a similar fate.

Of all the human organs we had to explore as medical students, the mind is the only one with no anatomy, only physiology, no structure, only function. There are no fixed points in the human mind. The skull is a hard protective case, but the brain tissue itself is porridgy – soft and floppy. The mind, which is what goes on inside the brain, is the most remarkable item in the universe – to suppose that it has limits, or fixities, or anything that remotely resembles bones or a skeletal structure, is to misunderstand what it is all about.

If you programme a computer – before you load the next programme you make sure that the memory, the RAM, is empty. The last thing you want is bits of the last programme mucking things up. The concept of empty RAM, a clean sheet on which to write your next programme, is fundamental to computing. The other fundamental is that you can write whatever you want – provided always you can fit the task in hand into the rather rigid strictures demanded by the binary digit, which is the very essence of the machine. Within this single proviso, the sky's the limit – you can construct whatever comes into your imagination.

The human mind is identical in this limited sense – it is empty. Ideas flood into it, doubtless even before birth, but none is more dominant than the others. The mind is an ideas organ – it is not blood which pulses through it, but thoughts. And, of course, emotions – which do the pulsing.

It is perfectly possible to empty the mind. It may be quite a challenge to do so, once we install certain fixed items of mental furniture, such as 'stick-close-to-Mum-if-you-want-to-live', but even these give themselves away by their very rigidity. The human mind is entirely plastic – it can take any shape you wish to allot it. Freud tried to tie down how the mind worked, to a whole series of other parts of the anatomy, the genitals, the anus, the breasts and so on – but the very plethora of such items bears witness to the failure of any one of them to dominate, or provide even half a suggestion that they are the 'heart' of the matter, or the very backbone.

Again, there is a fundamental misunderstanding. Too many people nowadays dip ever deeper into cerebral biochemistry with the object of bringing the whole organ under control. Genes are frantically sought – all with the avowed intent of bringing the aberrant human mind under control. The notion that is being sold is that once we get to the crux of the matter, then brain control will be ours, mind control will be there for the asking. Wrong. Wrong objective, wrong methodology, wrong values.

Control is already there. We control our own minds. We may make a hash of it, because of all those awesome emotions – but it is our mind, and our intent, which can keep it tidy or not. We already have self-determination. When our 'programming' or training, or early development goes awry, then we may find it more difficult – but the facility is there to be learnt and re-learnt. It will never be there with computers.

Computers Can't Think

Once computers start doing something extra to what they have been programmed to do, we send them to the workshop for repair. If they don't mend, we melt them down. Computers operate exclusively by their programme (when working as intended) – they would be quite useless if they did not. To suppose that they can take over this function is as ludicrous as supposing that your car can decide to drive itself to Glasgow, whether you will or no.

For the beauty of the computer is that it is as near a fully determined micro-universe as we are ever likely to see – and, on the whole, without imaginative human input, it is remarkably boring. Nothing happens inside a computer that has not been rigidly determined. Effect follows cause with a mathematical precision that is awesome, and oftentimes useful.

But this should emphasize that we are not like that. The mind is not a clockwork machine – the mind can make itself up, in a way that no computer ever can. That is what makes minds inherently interesting – and computers only of interest insofar as they reflect that. Minds take decisions, they are intrinsically self-determining. Computers make calculations and they are intrinsically other-determined.

Computers do not programme computers, any more than cars decide where they want to go. To programme anything, you have to have the ability to adapt, to respond to external events, in a way that defies the Second Law of Thermodynamics, as mentioned. Computers are under that Law – they are not alive and never will be. I don't know what living processes fundamentally are– but I know a dead machine when I see one.

A self-determined computer is therefore a contradiction in terms. And as we have seen earlier, a non-self-determined human tends to be unhappy, if not ill. There is the famous test devised by the computer pioneer Turing. He advises you to sit in a room with a terminal and try to guess whether the replies you get to the questions you type in arise from a machine or from a man or woman in the other room. This test accurately measures the gullibility of both testers and testees. Just take a look at the Test again. Here come the answers – you have to decide if they have been typed in directly by a human thence onto your screen, or typed in by a human into a computer, and only then on to your screen.

You are actually testing the ingenuity of the programmer. But to suppose that the machine could actually think up answers on its own is as ridiculous as supposing it will find a more 'creative' answer to the question 'What does 2 + 2 equal?'

Computers are the most intriguing invention of a highly inventive species. Yet they are actually no more than overgrown calculators – which does not make them any the less useful, but it does rule them out for ever from 'dominating' our lives, as human megalomaniacs try to do.

Human beings take decisions without a second thought. Will you have one lump or two?   Will you buy this item or that?

But think about it for a minute – in a fully determined universe such deciding is impossible – everything is predetermined. Inside a computer, for example, the decision as to whether to have one lump or two has to be programmed in. The machine looks in one spot for 'the answer' – if the answer in that spot is '2', then it prints '2', if it is '1', then '1'. If the answer is 'undetermined', that is not fixed by prior instruction, then it could be anything from 0 to 18,445,700,000,000,000,000 (18 quintillion) or more – which makes no sense either in or out of the machine.

Someone has to programme the machine. What a curious thing to have to write. The machine can never do this for itself. It is a false dream that many believe would solve all our problems. Computers can use programmes that have been written earlier – but not ones that have yet to be written. The only entity in the entire universe that can do that are living organisms – for some utterly unknowable reason, they run counter to the Second Law of Thermodynamics.

And here is the keyhole through which we humans can escape our earlier programming, our earlier training. We are capable of self-determination. We are capable of making up our own minds. We can take decisions on our own initiative. At first, these will be entirely parent-orientated – which makes sense, since no infant can survive without it. But later, as we grow up, we take over more and more of our own programming ourselves.

If we are responsible, we ensure that our actions impinge beneficially on those around us. We relate better and become more secure as we obtain feedback from our immediate kith and kin – those we meet can assist us by confirming our 'Sociability', our 'Lovability' – just as they can upset us by declining to do so.

The key is to move from infantile, essentially parent-orientated programming to adult, essentially interdependent programming. This is entirely possible to do. We programme computers and the computer jumps to our tune. We couldn't do any of this if we couldn't programme and reprogramme things, ourselves included.

Sadly, too many academic scientists, and psychiatrists do not even venture anywhere near this territory. Their view of humanity excludes the entire issue of whether they have a mind, or the capability of using it. Perhaps this in itself is some sort of irrationality. Either way, we each have to decide if it is True. Because if it isn't, then we are not obliged to Trust it. Nor need we Consent to such a belittling view of us human beings. So let's try and turn the topic around, and see if we cannot all grow up a little emotionally.

There's a Gene for It – So What?

Just because we suppose that there are genes which do things – as Mendel would say, giving some peas furry pods and others smooth pods – we need to be very much clearer about what we expect them to do for human beings, who, after all, are the main customers for this particular line of approach. If there is a gene for one particular type of behaviour, rather than another, then we need to be clear about what it would look like, and how we might expect it to work.

As human beings we can sit down, and 'brain storm' what we might wish to see happen. We think ahead, contemplating eventualities that were never there in our youth, certainly not in our parents' youth. Are we looking for genes to guide us with this type of issue?   How will an intimate knowledge of genes help us devise strategies to limit violent attacks or self-destructive diseases?

Or are we looking for genes to control us?   Are we looking for a gene to make a protein, which impacts on a receptor which makes us cool, calm and collected?   It's a bit like the house that Jack built – we go all round the houses, and the issue that really disturbs us, together with its solution, is sitting there all the while. For the issue of control has already been decided. We have intentions, which we move in certain chosen directions. These can lead to better self-control, via self-esteem, self-confidence and all the other virtues of Emotional Health. Or not.

Those who believe in determinism conclude that we do not have control in this sense, our notion of intent is illusory and there is no need to ensure we have Consent – coercion is all there is. So how is a knowledge of genetics going to help? How, once we have, for example, a gene for making secure and long lasting friendships – how can we implement it? Do we still have to override any interest in the process on the part of the guinea pig in question? Or must we, as argued elsewhere in this book, take their views into account, and operate by persuasion – much as we have to do without any genetic information whatsoever?

The pathway to emotional stability is not lined with DNA.

Born Evil or Born Lovable?

The commonest gene with respect to human behaviour that I have heard mentioned most is the one which supposedly leads to evil. 'Oh, he was born evil – you'll never do anything with him.' A significant number of prison officers held this view of the violent men in Parkhurst Prison Special Unit, when I began working there on 1 July 1991. It is understandable – especially if you come to work everyday never knowing which inmate is likely to attack you, burn you, stab you or scald you. Having no insight into the mechanisms which bring on these wanton destructions, it is understandable that you might call upon the dark forces of genetic diabolism.

Less forgivable is the position taken by today's psychiatric profession. In today's psychiatric bible, the DSM-IV (mentioned further in the appendix), the notion is set down in concrete that violent disorders are there from birth. The profession's face is turned away from the horrors of childhood trauma – they know from somewhere else that these dangerous individuals are that way because their genes tell them so. To use this as justification for doing absolutely nothing about the problem, for turning such dangerous individuals away from the clinic door because they are 'not mentally ill' – this is entirely reprehensible. What are doctors for, if not to assist all who seek their help? They may not succeed, but to hide behind pseudo-scientific nonsense about genetic influences, when childhood stress screams out to be taken notice of – this is unacceptable behaviour, in my view.

The notion that the prisoners who were my customers in Parkhurst Prison were born evil became ever less sustainable as time went by. At first there were fewer conspiracies. There was less bullying reported. And then the number of assaults went down. The tension on the wing eased. One visitor said that a parallel wing next door was like Beirut – at that time convulsed in internecine strife – compared to which, our Unit was peaceful normality itself. Not really what you would have expected, since entry to this Unit was restricted to those who were outstanding troublemakers and more violent than the norm. Then the inmates stopped ringing the alarm bells – there were fewer occasions which called for it – so too did the officers. Alarm bells are rung when you are attacked, or think you are about to be attacked, or see others in a similar predicament.

So what had happened? Had these inmates undergone a gene transplant? Were they privy to the relevant part of the human genome? This is not a trivial question. If these dangerous and manifestly violent individuals ceased being violent, then there is a lesson here for others to learn, should they be interested in finding the key to turning violence off.

The one thing about genes, and indeed the central motivation for researching them, is that they determine what happens to the organism they form part of. The reasoning being that, if we once found the supposedly 'evil gene', we could swap it for a different one, thereby ending our violence disease. But if violence evaporates without this genetic component being swapped over, or even modified in any respect whatsoever – then this raises serious questions.

It is not possible to have it both ways. Either you believe that violence is entirely genetic in origin and 'determined' by factors outside our control. Or that violence is not entirely genetic in origin – in which case vastly more effort needs to be directed at it, as a matter of urgency.

It is blandly assumed that, if an evil gene were ever found, then this would lead to health and happiness all round. Gaping holes appear in the argument – but these are swept away. However, if it should once be suggested that we already have all the equipment we need, that even without the enormous mound of data from the human genome in our grasp – we already know what to do – this vista becomes much more problematic and mired in hostile ideology.

Science has advanced largely by specializing. One difficulty with such specialization is that it becomes ever more difficult to integrate the various fields of activity. How can you acquire expertise in computers, brain chemistry, child development, psychiatry and psychology?   It becomes comparatively easy to hide behind these various subdivisions and isolate yourself from hard choices and difficult decisions.

Taking the broader view, however, there is abundant concrete evidence that we are in fact a Sociable species. We have sacrificed the standard mammalian tools for evolutionary survival, in favour of 'sociability'. Despite the ravages of the environment over the last three million years, the ice ages, the heat waves and various other impediments yet to come to light – despite all this, we have as a species not only survived, but flourished. There are more of us today than at any previous time in history.

This is direct evolutionary evidence in favour of our successful adaptation. I accept the story of the Aquatic Ape, which suggests that our bipedal posture resulted from standing on tiptoe in water up to our necks, not only to forage sea food better, but also to escape riparian predators. One reason for my especial interest is the thickening of a mother's hair before giving birth, and the clutch reflex which the newborn automatically operates on any hair that comes within reach. No other muscles are under the baby's control – yet this grip is fierce, automatic and unrelenting. Just what you would need to stop yourself floating off from the group when immersed.

It is also interesting to suppose that Homo sapiens's evolutionary handicap came from returning to dry land, where, instead of the water supporting the infant – there was that huge drop from the parent's shoulder to the hard ground. There is no parental fur to cling to, because, of course, hair slows swimmers down. No – once the supporting water dried up, so our childhood development proved to be our evolutionary Achilles heel.

There are those, like me, who still retain an optimistic view. For them it is self-evident that we are a Sociable species. Indeed we rather enjoy being Lovable – the impediment here not being genetic, but training. Which is why I am so enthusiastic about Emotional Health.

12 Pills and Potions – Tranquillizers, Anti-depressants or Talk?

Stress • Software Problems • The Role Chemistry and Hormones Really Play • Alcohol, Prozac and Testosterone

Psychiatry has explicitly and inexplicably turned its back on environmental factors in the causation of mental disease. It no longer concerns itself with nature and nurture, just nature. As mentioned, the term 'reaction', as in reacting to adverse social conditions, has been astonishingly excluded from the latest definitive text in psychiatry, the *DSM-IV.*(see Appendix). In my view, this tends to the view that human beings are best regarded as mindless unfeeling robots, which cannot be right. It has, again in my opinion, a profoundly deleterious effect on contemporary psychiatric practice.

Why should a psychiatrist bother to take a detailed social and emotional history, when he or she has been taught that your immediate or distant past experience has no bearing on the disease which brought you to him or her in the first place? Pure speculation. Your problem is essentially biochemical or biogenetic – this is the established view.

Why bother to find out what you yourself think about the problem, if there is nothing you can do about it? If you have no powers of choice or intent, then there is no way you could pull yourself together, even if you had the blueprint by which to do so. Taking a detailed history of events as they seem to
204

have occurred to the customer is seen as a waste of time for both parties.

The mind would seem to be the most appropriate human organ in which to house mental diseases – but if you are a trained psychiatrist, then you do not believe such an organ exists. In consequence you spend your time attempting to shoehorn all the symptoms presented to you into their bodily equivalents. Thus if depressive, you seek out changes in sleeping patterns or basal metabolic rates – if panicky, changes in hormonal influences.

Most psychiatrists have no truck with the emotions – you cannot weigh them, or even describe them very clearly, as we have seen – so, to be strictly 'scientific', they are not brought into the equation at any stage. Tranquillizers are clearly designed to reduce anxiety, they dull the sensation of fear. They remove the symptom, without the least knowledge of the root cause.

But if a psychiatrist showed the same disregard for pain as he or she does for emotion, he or she would be struck off the medical register. The worst thing you can do, as a doctor, is to give heavy doses of morphine to a patient with severe abdominal pain of uncertain origin. When the surgeon comes to examine that patient, all the symptoms have been erased – so there is no way to tell whether there has been a perforated gut, a thrombus in the lung or a heart attack – all of which call for rather different remedies.

Pain may be unpleasant, but it serves a vital function. Remember the last time your lip was anaesthetized at the dentist – did you chomp into it without knowing?   Removing symptoms may seem an admirable way to proceed – but only if you have no idea what the underlying disease really is and have no interest in finding out. Such prescribing obliterates not only the symptoms, but also all prospect of cure.

Fear, as discussed earlier, serves a similar life-saving function to pain. It always has a cause. The customer may not know what that is, but that is no reason for saying that there isn't one, or if there is, that it doesn't matter.

Tranquillizers are undoubtedly invaluable – but only when the underlying disease has been laid bare – otherwise you risk shutting up the whistle-blower, and with it, all warnings of worse disasters to come.

Emotions are not easy to describe, still less to control – but there is a way through that makes sense. It does not rely on biochemistry, nor on genetics.

Fears can be very painful – when their origins are totally obscure they may make life unbearable. But at least it pays to discuss them, to give them house-room.

Stress

The next item which established psychiatry teaches should be ignored is stress. The DSM-IV quoted in the appendix is quite outspoken on this point. Even 'death of a loved one' is explicitly excluded from established psychiatric consideration. This is actually at variance with a number of stress scales, which put death of spouse at number one. According to these scales, nothing is more stressful than having your partner die. And stress of this magnitude is no small item – a whole host of lesser diseases follow in its wake. Indeed it took me several years' hard learning in general practice to actually articulate the phrase 'stress is a killer' – but it's the Truth.

Psychiatrists today are taught that mental disease has no clear cause, and if it has, it is biogenetic – which doesn't help. Why should it be so easy to accept that if you increase the stress on a leg, for example, it breaks – but so difficult to apply the same to the mind? If you increase the stress on the mind, any mind, then in due course, above a certain threshold, that mind will fall to bits. We are none of us superman or superwoman – we are fallible human beings, and if you press us too hard, we break.

Conversely, when stress is decreased and support actively increased, the mind tends to repair itself as does any other human organ. One of the key stresses is feeling impotent – you have a problem thrust upon you but can see no means of resolving it. If the pressure is too high and the stakes a matter of life and death, then something is going to give.

This presupposes that we do have some ability to solve some problems. We do have a modicum of ability to respond to challenges in our environment. We may not manage to solve them all, but we can, in principle, solve more than none. And if we can solve even a handful, it means that what we strive for, what we intend to do – this matters, this counts, this can make a difference, even if only now and again.

Behind this solving-ability is the responding-ability mentioned earlier. Living organisms on this planet have shown a remarkable ability to adapt and change – they partake in evolution. Now this caused consternation two centuries ago, when Darwin first suggested it to a God-fearing populace. In this century we need to take the matter a step further forward, and claim that we have a remarkable ability to adapt our environment to us. In this way we can solve problems. We can evolve a way through them.

This passes here under the label 'intent', which, however difficult it is to define, is something without which you cannot be sane. Further, if your most pressing emotional problems seem utterly insoluble and inflict savage depressions upon you, then pause. Ask someone who has an interest in emotional conflicts, an awareness that there are hidden emotions, such as 'frozen terrors' – which are from long ago and far away, at least they are when you can see them straight.

But do not expect conventional psychiatrists to show even the least interest in this topic. It simply has no relevance for his or her treatments. Psychiatrists have been firmly taught that what we need are better biochemists, ever more potent brain drugs. In fact many psychiatrists are really brain doctors in disguise. Delving more deeply into ever smaller recesses of brain tissue may seem a respectable activity, but if the problem is not hardware, but software, you may be hazarding your customers with ever more powerful chemical agents for little reliable gain.

Every customer for psychiatric services should be asked, 'Would you like to be shown ways of pulling yourself together?', perhaps by market research. For the conventional psychiatric profession this is not only a total irrelevance, but goes deeper. It actually questions the ideology of psychiatry. This may sound far-fetched – but not if your experience of conventional psychiatry has been unhappy.

Software Problems

The last point of contention – software – is perhaps the most potent. If mental diseases are essentially software problems – then that is where they should be tackled, since if they are not tackled there, no amount of tinkering with the hardware will assist, indeed it is almost guaranteed to make matters worse.

Software is training, it is how we are programmed, from the first moment we have a mind which can absorb facts, findings and instructions. Minds are more unlike computers than fish are from bicycles – but both do need to be fed simple instructions to start with, before they can move on to more advanced, more complex tasks.

If mental disorders are software disorders, then we need psychiatrists and others who take this as their fundamental starting point. One of the difficulties is that conventional psychiatrists have reacted unfavourably to Dr Freud, overreacted in fact. Freud's fanciful phantasies are not helpful. But to throw out the whole process of talk therapy just because a nineteenth-century neurologist got it wrong is to cut off your customers at the ears.

To be able to talk your customers through their problems, you need to know more about those problems than your customers did when they first came to see you. Further you need to have confidence in those areas where your customers have none – else you will be as fearful of their 'buried terrors' as they are, and then it could be the blind leading the blind.

But if the answer to the above market-research question turned out to be 'yes' – then the psychiatric profession would need to repair its current deficits and find ways of answering its customers' demands. How do you provide road maps for those who wish to pull themselves together? If you were to ask me, I would prescribe a large dose of Truth, Trust and Consent to enable you to pursue the notion of being Lovable, Sociable and Non-violent – all in the cause of furthering Emotional Health, which of course is the aim of the book in the first place.

Scientific Credibility - The Role Chemistry and Hormones Really Play

Let's recap. The five bones of contention with modern psychiatry are simply stated – intent, mind, emotions, stress and software. Simple to state, impossible to define. In terms of an orthodox scientific viewpoint, this is not a strong position.

For a start, let's define our terms. However reasonable that might seem, I can't – I just cannot say what I mean, precisely, by any one of them. I simply don't know. Next, there is not a shred of concrete tangible evidence to suggest that any of them even exists, let alone that they are the most important part of every human being that ever lived. Scientifically speaking, therefore, there is just no measurable objective evidence to support the contention in the first place.

Intent exists in courts of law – but since when were lawyers paragons of scientific progress and reasoning? The evidence for intent is as thin as the air we breathe. The mind has long been in dispute – it is entirely intangible, it is forever a hypothesis – nothing concrete has ever been proven about the mind – we don't even really know with any precision where it 'is'. As for the emotions, there is more evidence for the existence of gale-force winds than there is for these airy creations. Stress differs for each one of us – so how can you even begin to devise a 100 per cent objective scientific definition for it?   And software – everyone knows what it is meant to do, but despite repeated attempts over the past half century – the production of a reliable, scientific way of writing new software has continued to defeat even the best brains in the business – there just isn't one. Could it be that software and science are also on a collision course?

Furthermore, by suggesting that living processes breach the Second Law of Thermodynamics, I am certainly not courting scientific orthodoxy. People who advocate breaking the scientific law of the day, whether by suggesting that the sun does not really rotate around the world or that Newtonian time and space are not really absolute, can expect a hard time. Einstein gained credibility only when the sun's gravity bent a beam of light. The Uncertainty Principle is even more unsettling for Homo sapiens, since in essence it says that you can tell where an electron is going, but not where it is, or vice versa, never both. So unless there were substantial practical benefits from this impossible conundrum, it would have been given short shrift and stored away on the back shelf along with magnetic unipoles and the subdivisions of a quark.

But the Uncertainty Principle offers us a glimmer of comfort – for though it runs entirely counter to logic, and utterly and indelibly defies our understanding – it works. A whole string of new electronic devices actually relies on the probability that an electron can be any old place – not that it is, but that it could be. These are the notorious 'tunnelling' electrons – like anarchic maggots, they burrow through the bedrock of our possible understanding, extinguishing for ever our ability to 'know' – yet they are not only tolerated, they are welcomed – they work. They allow things to happen and to be built that would be quite inconceivable without them. Rather what I would claim for the five bones above.

In a significant sense, I am trying to strike a bargain here. If science does not support these five points, then you must also accept the current psychiatric orthodoxy that we are essentially mindless, unfeeling robots or automatons – we have no other building blocks to play with. However, if you will just come with me for a little way down this pathway I have found through the morass, you may feel tempted to look at your everyday world through slightly less rigid 'scientific', more humane eyes.

Alcohol, Prozac and Testosterone

Take alcohol, for instance. I speak figuratively of course. Alcohol has an effect on the mind. The chemistry is well known. Alcohol is a partial breakdown product in the metabolism of sugar – it is what is left after yeast has done the best it can with it. The molecule itself has almost as many calories as sugar, and goes everywhere in the body that sugar goes. When it gets to the brain, it disconcerts the cells there – perhaps they were expecting the full glucose molecule.

You and I know what alcohol does to the mind – some of us see far too much of it. But do you see this?   What you see is decided by what you expect to see. If you expect 'clockwork' mechanisms, then the alcohol and the chemistry are paramount. If not, what then?

Just suppose that a man or woman with alcohol circulating in the blood tried to resist its well-known soporific and intoxicating effects. Is it possible? Surely once a brain is steeped in alcohol, that's it – the chemical takes over, there is nothing further we can do.

But wait – are there not stories of drunks sobering up? Tipsy individuals suddenly trying to pull themselves round to face the music? In an earlier chapter the case of Stan was mentioned, in which a significant item survived the well-known amnesic effects of excess alcohol – this has relevance here. Of course, once they are unconscious, then they might as well be dead, from the viewpoint of this experiment. But before that, when alcohol is circulating and the mind is already dulled – what can possibly be happening which alters the chemistry?

If you take the view that we are essentially chemical machines – the answer is simple – nothing happens. A drunk is a drunk is a drunk. But if you once let in the notion that we can have intent, we can express a purpose, we can strive – then an addition to the chemistry must be made. Not only do we have the disabling effects of the alcohol, we also have the enabling effects of intent.

Human beings, in this view, are not mere machines. They have a mind, they have emotions, they have intentions. We may get fearfully muddled, but the reality is that we are not mere chemical factories. We can think, with varying degrees of opacity – and however great our limitations, we can nudge our biochemical characteristics one way or another. Even if the effect is minuscule, if it occurs once, then it can occur again. If we once defy the Second Law of Thermodynamics, even to a microscopic degree – what can we not do?

What is true for alcohol is true for all other chemicals which gain access to and impede the functioning of our brains. Testosterone has been blamed for many things. It is supposed to turn men into bulls, or at least into pigheaded boors. And I know from personal experience that it grows beards and deepens the voice. But does it run the man? Does it call the tune?   Can we awkward males do little to resist the call of the wild, or the testosteronic high jinks to which our gonads goad us?

These chemical questions receive clear answers from the scientific and indeed the psychiatric establishments – chemistry rules, forget your notions of autonomy, of responsibility, of intent or independence. You are the result of your genes and your chemicals – there is nothing you can do about it.

From this, it follows that most psychiatric endeavours are chemically orientated. There have even been unfortunate suggestions that anti-depressants, such as Prozac or the tricyclics, be put in the drinking water – heaven preserve us. Almost as lunatic as suggesting we do the same with opiates, so that none of us would ever feel any pain.

Breaking the Second Law of Thermodynamics is only a temporary affair. It is not so much breaking it as bending it, or deferring it for a brief while. If we cease to adapt to our surroundings, or cease evolving to cope with environmental challenges – we cease. Disorganization or entropy increases everywhere – except inside living cells – and it increases there, immediately we die.

So there is only a brief respite. If we decide we are chemical machines, and put our developmental resources and energies into that strategy – then this has consequences, not all of which will necessarily be quite so admirable.

Drugs, chemicals, pills and potions may certainly assist – I recommend them to my customers on the same terms I would recommend they use a crutch if they broke a leg. But they do not represent a cure – the disease entity they are applied to is in a different category. The crutch can be useful, invaluable – but if it hinders the leg healing, it will prove a disservice. Similarly with chemicals – if they distract attention from the real problem, then they will cripple even more than the disease they were intended to assist.

The Second Law of Thermodynamics can only be resisted as long as we exercise our ability to respond, our responding-ability, our responsibilities. This notion that we can, to however small a degree, counteract an otherwise universal physical law carries a cost – unless we continue our intentions in a responsible and realistic fashion, then our brief heyday will be even briefer than it need have been.

So the question whether or not we have intent, or are chemical machines, has implications for our longer term survival. Irresponsibility, whether ignoring inconvenient evidence or insisting on established views when there is dissent – irresponsibility, whatever the cause, decreases survivability.

As may be clear from the earlier parts of this book, the emotions play a major role in mental disease, in depression, personality disorders and elsewhere. Emotional Education has been mentioned as a pathway to Emotional Health, as a way to mental health. The question as to whether it is or not is one to be decided by each customer in turn.

This, of course, presupposes that such customers have a choice, that they do indeed have the capability of intent. If they don't, then the issue is closed. But if they do, then describing psychiatric problems as software not hardware has implications for every aspect of society, not least its longevity. For Emotional Health impinges directly on our evolution, on our evolutionary strategies, which, in the long or even the remarkably short run, determine how long it will be before we all become extinct.

13 Psychiatry – Legal and Illegal

The Law Court as Social Destroyer • Trust Me, I'm a Doctor? • The Illegality of Untreatability • There's No Pill, So You're Not Ill • The Illegality of 'Electric Shock Treatment' • If the TV Doesn't Work, Fix It by Throwing It Downstairs • 'Lock them up and throw away the key' • Under the Carpet Is Still in the Room • What about the Victim, for Pity's Sake?

You have just turned the corner. You had been through a rocky patch, when nothing seemed to go right. You were in trouble with the police and ended up in a mental hospital. But that was six months ago, and since then things have begun to settle. You are getting on much better with your present girlfriend, Freda, and indeed you would already be married, except you couldn't afford it this month. You might think that 19 was a little young to embark upon matrimony, but you know what it is like to come from a broken home, so you are determined not to let this happen to your children. You are both delighted that Freda is now pregnant – and you both look forward to your adopting her two-year-old daughter as your own. At last the future begins to look brighter than ever before.

You are settling down to have the first Christmas for as long as you can remember, with your family, your new family in this case. There is a knock at the door on Christmas Eve. Your two year old step-daughter is removed by Social Services. You are instructed not to see Freda. The little girl is removed to a 'place of safety'. A rumour circulates that you might 'snatch' the girl, so her access to Freda, her mother, is restricted to three hours a week. Staffing shortages mean that in practice even this is curtailed. Your world collapses.

What is going on? Can this be a civilized country? The draconian powers of the forthcoming Mental Health Act have not yet been enacted. You have committed no crime, you have hit none of the parties to the case. You have no history of damaging children. You have arguments with Freda, but unlike before, you sort them out – and you are beginning to build a life for all three of you. The case comes to court. You lose. Though none of the parties involved has been convicted of any crime, Freda is ordered to chose between you and her daughter. She is ordered to go live in a hostel for three months, to prove that she can live without you. If she does not, then she will not see her daughter again.

The Law Court as Social Destroyer

This is a true story. It occurred in England, recently. Let's call the man Mike. The legal basis for it is about to be tightened yet further, so that even grosser miscarriages of justice can be guaranteed. The scope for misplaced fears, misaligned punishments and other malpractices, grows.

The judge in Mike's case did not like my report, even from the outset, before he had set eyes on me or I on him. He 'ordered' me to produce a codicil, to appear in court, to produce my clinical notes – he obviously took me for an awkward customer and adjusted his courtroom setting to take this into account. He rearranged the seating plan to give me a prominent place at the very front, where his intention had clearly been to roast me as a troublesome eccentric. What had clearly upset him was my court report, which gave an unconventionally humane account of why Mike had been violent, and how he had now overcome it. My distress at being subject to judicial coercion was as nothing compared to the travesty which was enacted before my astonished eyes.

The upshot was that Mike, the 19-year-old, from whom his two-year-old step-daughter was adjudged to need legal protection, was regarded, as the DSM-IV mentioned earlier lays down, as incapable of change. Accordingly he had no defence. No matter that the psychiatrist who was representing the social services had not seen Mike for nine months, by the time of the trial. The diagnosis remained unchanged, indeed unchangeable. On cross-examination Mike was freely declared to be untreatable. It was loosely opined that nine years in Broadmoor might be acceptable, except, Catch-22, he had already been rejected thence, because he was 'untreatable'. The prospect of amelioration had thereby been eliminated.

Evidence for precisely such amelioration was produced at the trial – but neither judge nor psychiatric expert paid the slightest attention – their minds had been made up many months, if not years, before. Mike, his future in tatters, attempted suicide. What would you do?

Fears, as we have noted, impel a host of irrationalities and indeed prejudices, or prejudgements. Here we have judicial fears, social fears and so on. But the remedy for all fears, real or imagined, is greater realism, a better grasp of the reality of the situation in hand.

Suppose Mike had attacked Freda – he had a history of being violent. Suppose he had attacked the little girl – he had no history of doing so, but this point was dismissed by the social services' psychiatrist. What a disaster this would have proved, for all those involved with the care proceedings before it happened.

So this is the dilemma. The risk is clear, actual harm could well be caused to the child. This exists as a possibility – it hasn't happened yet, so we don't know for certain – but it is there as a risk – the harm from Mike is there, but remains hypothetical. However, the harm to the two-year-old resulting from depriving her of parental contact is obvious, absolutely guaranteed, and already being inflicted. Three months is a long time for a two-year-old. The judge acknowledged this point to me in court, in passing, but paid it no heed, and omitted it from his judgement.

In England, as this judge knew, the powers available to him predate any criminal act on the part of the potential abuser. Fears voiced by any significant individual can invoke fearsome legal interventions – up to and including statutory parental deprivation.

Application of our clumsy legal processes to such delicate family matters is bound to inflict damage. There are vastly better ways of going about these very real problems. The elimination of child physical abuse by means of improved family support as demonstrated in the project by Yale University has already been mentioned. Why apply quasi-criminal proceedings when we already have available clear social support strategies which eliminate the problem?   Who can be comfortable with the outcome described here, when healthier alternatives are well established and have proved their worth elsewhere? Much play is made of the notion that ignorance of the law is no excuse – perhaps ignorance of social realities should carry an equivalent judicial reprimand.

Here we have a family court which pays the crucial importance of the family no heed – a nascent family is not supported, guided and assisted to a more stable life and thence a more stable society. This family-to-be has been destroyed.

Trust Me, I'm a Doctor?

If you had difficulties with your more violent emotions, would you go to a doctor to seek assistance?   You might think twice about going if you knew that your condition was regarded as entirely biogenetic, that it would be labelled 'permanently untreatable' – a label that would hang round your neck poisoning any future contact you might have with the law. Had that psychiatrist not sent a report to the Social Services, unasked – then Mike's case would never have arisen.

How can this be a sensible way of proceeding?   If we, as a society, are concerned to protect young children from obvious violent threats – we need to take a much harder look at what actually goes on. Our children are our future – if we neglect them, we perish. But if we are too clumsy, then we damage them anyway.

It is difficult to envisage enlightened legislation being enacted in this area. The legislation currently under review gives ever more coercive and unevaluated powers to psychiatry. Fears are fanned, rather than evaluated; remedies are dismissed, rather than subjected to cost-effective analysis. We live in a coercive society, which ignores that fact that consensus offers far more stability.

Let's be quite clear about it – if you cannot control yourself, if you harbour wishes to become a rapist, a grievous bodily harmer, or serial killer – then you cannot expect society to allow you to flourish and visit your destructivities on all and sundry. If, for example, you were about to throw yourself, or anyone else, out of a fifth floor window – I would exert all the physical coercion available to me to prevent you doing what you wanted. I would seek to deprive you, as strenuously as I could, of your Consent in the matter.

I would have no problem with this. I would strain every muscle to prevent you exercising your own personal choice – you would, in the terms of the Mental Health Act (1983) be risking harm to yourself or others. You would thereby have lost your right to be regarded as a stable, sensible, responsible adult. And I would grab you and hold you as long as need be, just as I would any (other) infant about to perform the same lunacy.

But I would not regard this as anything more than a short-term measure. If I left it at that, I would be little better than the barons in the Middle Ages on whose whim you could languish for decades in a dank dungeon. No – even as I sat on your head, I would open negotiations as to the origin of this destructive motivation. I would seek to sort out why, in all the world, you wished to end everything. I would even start to suggest something along the lines of being born Lovable, Sociable and Non-violent, and begin to fan into flame a few sparks of Truth, Trust and Consent from which a furnace might eventually grow which could consume all the irrationality underlying your misperception. This worked well enough in Parkhurst Prison – why not apply it more widely?

But it may take some time to achieve this happier state. I would like to see the day when no violent act, or future violent act, passes unremarked, untreated and uneliminated. It turns on what sort of society we wish to live in. And on how we view our fellow men and women. But what is needed most of all is a reconsideration of how we view mental disease. If the current orthodoxy prevails, then more enlightened views will invariably take a backward seat.

As I see it, our most realistic approach is a wholistic one – every part of us is actually just one aspect of a single living organism. The same concept applies on a wider scale. Our society is also a single organism, and needs to be treated holistically. Thus we cannot apply coercion willy-nilly in one bit, if we wish to encourage autonomy, and responsible adult behaviour in another. Emotional Health, on this reading, applies to us all.

The Illegality of Untreatability

When I was a medical student we used to joke that when a doctor (or medical student) couldn't make head or tail of what was going on, there was a simple recourse – reach into your medical bag, fish out the label 'psychopath' and pin it decisively on to the patient. This disguised the problem of doctor ignorance and loaded everything on to customer failure. Medical honour was preserved. Forty years on, it is a shock to find this wretched principle enacted into legislation.

How can you begin to say which is the better treatment – when the doctors themselves say there is no treatment? Where's the evaluation of the doctor's view?   Where's the scouring of every corner of the earth for even the slightest whisker of a remedy?   If even one sufferer starts to recover – where are the legions of medical personnel desperate for a breakthrough in this most dismal corner of medical practice?

If only one anorexic starts eating, only one Dangerous Severe Personality disorder (DSPD) stops violating, only one Borderline Personality disorder (BPD) stops insisting on burning themselves with their live cigarettes – if any one of these happy ameliorations occurred, where are the battalions of researchers evaluating, probing, finding out and publishing this prodigious therapeutic anomaly?   In a world where nothing works (or is expected to work), even a single swallow would make a glorious summer.

Customers enter a contract with their supplier. Here customers for psychiatric services are told service has been discontinued. If you set up as a doctor, you undertake to assist. If you then arbitrarily exclude those you cannot understand, then clearly you are in breach. Worse, if you then label those seeking your help as 'not mentally ill', then you shrink your area of responsibility yet further. Is there no legal limit to this shrinkage?

Untreatable. What a dreadful foxhole for any profession to hide itself in. Let's look at a real untreatable disease. If I am faced with someone in a diabetic coma, and have no available insulin, then that person will be dead within the week. That is untreatability. You don't need a double-blind trial to legitimize the use of insulin if it saves lives so dramatically. But you do need to look at the problem with an open mind.

If a business goes bankrupt, it can redeem itself over time, by succeeding commercially where previously it failed. If a profession goes bankrupt, a similar process of redemption is surely available – after all, we all need doctors, and especially doctors of the mind, that most important of all human organs. But what if the profession is now closed?

Self-harm is the final nail in the orthodox psychiatric coffin. Self-harmers display a motivation to reverse the normal healing process – they pull the stitches out of self-inflicted wounds sutured by hard-working surgeons. There is a way through this dangerous morass, as discussed, but it involves rather more bones of contention than are customarily tolerated. If you overheard what passes for medical 'reasoning' you too would be appalled. 'This patient has had a year to respond to treatment. She's no better – she has failed to take advantage of what we have offered, so should be discharged.'   'If you wish to leave hospital, you must gain at least two pounds (1 kilo) by Tuesday – else we will forcibly detain you.'

No service can hope to survive which blames the customer for its own failings. This is a failure by the profession to take a broad enough view, to open its eyes to the abundant literature on childhood trauma, and malattachment in infancy. The mental supplicant is already enfeebled – how can they turn the tables?   If they knew how to behave in a healthy way – they would need no such coercive 'contract' to do so.

If you seriously believe that human beings are mindless, unfeeling robots – then it must seem entirely appropriate that you seek ever more refined mechanical means to remedy their abundant mental woes. Perhaps a course in existential epistemology might assist you in coming to a more balanced judgement – but how many medical curricula would stretch this far.

There's No Pill, So You're Not Ill

The problem with viewing human beings as chemical machines is that if your remedies do not work, there is a dreadful temptation to suggest that the customer in front of you is not ill. If your standard approach is unsuccessful, clearly that particular client does not fall within the range of those who generally do respond. Once your profession has drunk from the cup of customer culpability, what is there to stop you suggesting that if there is no pill for your client, then he or she is not ill?

These are not minor adjustments, small alterations in the nomenclature. These problems are vast, unbridgeable and fundamental. Do we have intent? Can we chose? Are emotions anything to do with it? Do minds matter? Should environmental stress be readmitted to the medical pantheon? No wonder there are so many consultant psychiatric vacancies.

I well remember my first psychiatric professional meeting – in 1958. There was a discussion after the main talk, and it divided the congregation into two. One man stoutly declared that all depression was caused by factors from within, it was endogenous – another equally strongly maintained that it was reactive – it resulted from a reaction to some external happening or event. Sadly, the former have won the battle, though it turns out the latter were right all along.

Reading the preamble to the DSM-IV, it is clear that after 1952 a conscious decision was taken to remove from serious psychiatric consideration all those conditions which were directly related to environmental factors.

In this morning's post, I received a letter from Rita Udall, a friend of mine who is an Adlerian therapist. Rita knew I was writing this book, so she enclosed a letter from one of her customers, part of which runs as follows:

> 'I feel there are elements in conventional psychiatric treatment which promote a false sense of security, an invitation to withdraw into unreality, a relinquishment of personal responsibility, a loss of self worth, a passive acceptance of helplessness, a desire to be labelled and categorised, an unfulfilling dependency and regression, a mistaken notion of illness, a progressive manifestation of symptoms and a loss of autonomy.'

The mind is invisible and intangible. Evidence from those who are or who have been mentally ill can be minimized, or overlooked. But if we can once institute better democratic channels whereby the voice of even the least powerful is heard, then I anticipate we would hear a great deal more criticism of conventional psychiatry, along these lines.

Happily, the whole tangled problem is remediable. It is not easy, else it would have been done long ago. But by widening our perspectives, collecting views from as many as we can – then in a healthier democracy, inhumane practices, from whatever profession, can be highlighted and eliminated. To illustrate just one such inhumane practice we turn now to the modern equivalent of the mediaeval ducking stool.

The Illegality of 'Electric Shock Treatments'

You are a thrusting young engineer. Your career is going well. You are as keen as mustard – indeed some might almost regard your attention to detail and your insistence on precision as obstreperous – though these qualities can otherwise be quite admirable in any engineer. You take especial delight in exploded diagrams – those drawings which show a gearbox or other contrivance as if hit by a bomb, with parts apparently flying off in all directions. This is particularly useful in your line of work, and you are climbing the promotion ladder with gusto.

Sadly, there are tensions at home to which you fail to pay enough attention. So you fall out with your wife. She leaves you. This shakes you severely. Matters are not helped by an attack of what might be glandular fever, during which you develop hallucinations and are admitted to a psychiatric ward.

You are advised to have Electric Shock Treatment, also known as Electro Convulsive Therapy or ECT. You object. You demand to see your solicitor. Your objections are overruled. You are given ECT under a section of the Mental Health Act. You are given this invasive treatment under coercion. You did not give your Consent – but received the treatment anyway.

It is an open question whether every Consent form for ECT should carry words to the effect that 'I have been fully informed, and made entirely aware of the fact that passing electric currents through my brain tissue can leave permanent damage. I am also aware that there have been a number of recent cases where severe and long lasting mental impairment has resulted directly from this treatment such as the inability to read or to tell the time. Despite all these risks having been carefully explained to me and to my next of kin, I still wish this treatment to be given me.'

Could it be argued in a court of law that Consent forms without words like these appearing on them are not legally valid?   Fully informed Consent is the legal rule. Without such words being there, have those consenting to ECT been fully informed?   Has the psychiatric profession fully informed itself of the nature of this abominable treatment?

If the TV Doesn't Work, Fix It by Throwing It Downstairs

The evidence against ECT is abundant. Again, it may be difficult for those untrained in the ways of psychiatry to appreciate just how bizarre this so-called remedy actually is. Let's take a more familiar situation. You are sitting there, watching your favourite TV programme, and then the darned set breaks down again. You check the power socket – it looks all right. You give the box an encouraging nudge – still nothing. So you pick the thing up and toss it downstairs. Would you really do this?   Wouldn't you take far more care of your TV set than this?   It doesn't even appear to be a halfway sensible approach to a malfunctioning TV. Why should a similar 'bash it and see' approach have any more merit in psychiatry?

Let's call this young engineer Tom. We find irrefutable evidence that Tom's brain has been damaged by ECT. Exploded diagrams are a thing of the past – Tom can no longer retain any sense of spatial geometry in his mind at any one time. It could be argued that he has just 'gone off', or that he was never really that good in the first place. Then, when Tom reads through a blockbuster – War and Peace or Shogun, for example – he can reread them all again in six months, since in the meantime he has entirely forgotten the plot. But again, a clever barrister could make out that this was all in the imagination.

So what about telling the time?   Give Tom a clock face with the hands pointing to six o'clock, and he tells the time like an expert. Put the hands at 4:21 and he is stumped. He cannot tell the time. He puzzles, he wrestles, he grimaces, he asks if he can skip the test. Now it would seem to me that a young engineer who was progressing well could not have done so had he been unable to tell the time – ergo his inability to tell the time has been inflicted upon him by the ECT.

Next is the *medical* argument to end all ECTs – which any practising doctor should know, and be aware of. The argument is in the form of a triangle, each leg of which is irrefutable and joins its brethren in a watertight manner. Firstly then, there is no dispute but that the sole aim of ECT is to induce a convulsion. This is a full scale epileptic fit. In the very early days these fits were produced by drugs, but nowadays they are triggered by electric currents. So ECT induces convulsions.

The second leg takes a leaf out of the history of epilepsy. There is no way of escaping the fact that the key diagnostic sign for epilepsy, to distinguish it unerringly from, say, a faint (or 'syncope', to use the medical term), is the presence of amnesia or memory loss. Epilepsy generates amnesia.

The third leg therefore links these two as follows – since ECT invariably gives rise to an epileptic fit, and since epilepsy invariably gives rise to amnesia – it follows inexorably that ECT induces amnesia or memory loss. My view is that the customer forgets what it was that was causing the depression, and that this amnesia is all that can be said to explain why ECT 'works'. Perhaps they forget how 'unlovable' they always thought they were – or perhaps it knocks the edge off their mental acuity, so they care less. Either way it is entirely reprehensible.

Epilepsy is also well known to inflict brain damage in its own right. Boxers render their opponents unconscious, and, in doing so, invariably cause microscopic tissue damage – epilepsy whether spontaneous or electrically induced, does the same. Evidence from laboratory animals, both cats and dogs, given a series of ECTs, shows clear neurological damage in those areas of the brain immediately underlying the electrodes. What else would you expect? There has been much discussion of the effects of mobile-phone radiation on brain tissue – with ECT, electric currents are deliberately passed through the brain, in order to give it another disease – epilepsy. Is this in any way sensible?

If you react to the notion of sticking electrodes on the skull and sending enough electricity through the brain to induce convulsions, with nausea – then you are surely right to do so. Perhaps you would join with me in trying to render it illegal, or at least making it mandatory to obtain the Consent of two further independent medical advisers, one of whom should be an epileptologist or at least a neurologist.

At a recent count it was found that 65,000 doses of ECT are currently being given every year in this country. Certainly at a hospital which regards itself as a pioneering psychiatric institution, where I recently worked for six months, a new patient was started on this medieval treatment every two months on average. For a pioneer this leaves something to be desired.

The standard conventional psychiatric reply is that this unusually invasive treatment is quite essential to save lives. But surely there are not 65,000 acutely suicidal mental patients every year? Depression can be a lethal disease, but not all these 65,000 recipients are going to die without it.

Psychiatry is bereft of ideas. It has shown itself content with declaring large chunks of its clientele 'not mentally ill', and even more as 'untreatable'. The effects of this almost wishful ignorance is to ensure that we have a decidedly lower standard of justice than we deserve. We also have a profession which should long ago have thrown out ECT on the grounds that it doesn't even approach being a reasonable, respectable or responsible treatment – since no one has the slightest idea how it works, and everyone should have a clear idea what damage electrically induced epilepsy necessarily inflicts.

As for the alternatives – these have been highlighted earlier in this book. If you don't find the propositions presented here congenial, you are left with the standard psychiatric approach, which can picture us only as mindless, unfeeling robots. If you restrict yourself to this narrow vision, then ECT becomes inevitable – it is the only recourse left when the ever more potent chemicals prescribed as anti-depressants fail.

So do not be surprised to have this medieval shock therapy suggested for you or yours – it follows naturally from the limited view that psychiatry has of us human beings. In my view ECT is an abomination and should be outlawed forthwith. It stands as the direct antithesis to Truth, Trust and Consent and scarcely begins to touch on the intrinsic nature of humanity, which surely tries to come ever closer to being Lovable, Sociable and Non-violent. At least it does if it aspires to becoming Emotionally Healthy.

The bankruptcy of psychiatry is highlighted too where it impinges on the prison system, to which we now turn.

'Lock them up and throw away the key'

You have not been doing too well recently. You've lost your job, have nowhere to go, sleeping rough, getting by with small-scale burglary and petty pilfering. You are still young and very strong – if you could get it together, you'd be fine. But let's face it, you are down and out. For some reason you take it into your head to walk to Oxford with your mate Nick. Things do not go well. You break into a house, but are disgusted to find 'only pennies' – dismal. So you decide to walk back home, a distance of a hundred miles or so. You have to concede that this is not a well-planned strategy, but your life has been chaotic for a while now, and you see little prospect of improvement.

By the time you get back to your home town, you are at the end of your tether. You and Nick are scarcely on speaking terms. It's November time, and getting very cold. You hole up in some derelict building and try to keep warm by burning all available woodwork, door frames, window frames, anything burnable that comes to hand.

At this point matters take a tragic turn. Nick is cold too, and starts whining at you to go down the road to where your mother lives. 'At least we'll be warm,' he says. You curse him, and try to explain in a twisted logic that you never take your criminal friends home. This makes little sense, as Nick wastes no time in telling you. He does not stop. As the cold takes a firmer grip, so he builds the pressure for you to return to your mother's. To him, nothing could be more straightforward – a simple, if temporary, solution to an increasingly pressing and ever chillier problem.

You will hear none of it. You are not clear why, but powerful emotional blockages are stirring in your mind to prevent you taking the course of action your companion advocates. He insists, you resist – something has to give. Finally you snap. Out of control, you pick a quarrel and knock him down. You knock him out, and start battering him – and you don't stop. You have no clear idea why you started and none at all as to why you should stop. Shortly after, you have put an end to his pestering for ever – Nick is dead.

None of the 60 murderers I got to know well in Parkhurst Prison knew why they killed. It's not so much 'who-dunnit?' but 'why-dunnit?'   When you come to trial, the judge is just as much in the dark. You are persuaded to plead insanity or 'diminished responsibility' – there being nothing else that can account for the crime to which you pleaded guilty. The judge opines that a sentence of seven years would fit the occasion – but that was in 1980, and the prospect of your being released recedes every year. No one gives a thought to Nick and his bereaved family.

Here the law is leaning on psychiatry at its weakest point – inevitably both professions suffer as a result, as we saw earlier. Established psychiatry doesn't know where Dangerous Severe Personality disorders (DSPD) come from, or even very clearly what they are. The law goes by the letter, takes psychiatric mumbo-jumbo as gospel and metes out injustice accordingly.

Let's call the murderer in the above case Larry. We worked out together that his mother had 'battered' him as a child, and that it was the hidden terror of her that prevented his returning to the warmth of her home. He did not know this at the time. But later, 11 years later, when he did, he said – *'If this had've happened years ago, where a doctor had taken an interest – say when I was in my twenties – and said what you'd said and we'd conquered it, and then I went into the house. And say I came in late, and she said blah blah blah and she went to hit me, I'd say mother you can't hit me Love – I'm a grown up. You can't do it.'* After thinking through what was previously unthinkable, Larry's fear of his mother had evaporated. As he says, had he had the opportunity to talk things through, he would have '*conquered it*' – and murder would never have been on the agenda.

However, having fallen foul of the medico-legal morass, there is now no way out for him. He is looking at 40 years in prison, despite what the trial judge adjudicated – at £25,000 a year, that will cost society £1,000,000. I know him well, and were it not for my being banned by the government, could vouch for his complete safety. Other psychiatrists do not, and so cannot. Without public and professional confidence, Larry remains a risk – an 'untreatable' risk – and is therefore 'unreleasable'.

Under the Carpet is Still in the Room

How easy to pretend that Larry, and all similar problems, do not exist – sweep them under the carpet, build more prisons, spend more on penal institutions than on educational ones. Prisons, however, are part of society too – they are thermometers of our social health, or in this case ill health.

Let's look at what the law courts are set up to do. What the criminal justice system should be doing is protecting us, the innocent public. In a rational world it would be audited (as The Economist newspaper suggested some 35 years ago) – checks, feedback and data would be collected and communicated, to see if what the system did, worked. Every judge or sentencer would then have a track record, to show him or her, and the public whose servant she is, just how successful their actions had been in reducing the threat to our life, limb and property. That is, what happened next?

What about the Victim, for Pity's Sake?

Were such a simple and practical data-log in operation, Larry and all his ilk would be earning his keep rather than costing us all. But, above all, were all citizens given an effective voice, which is what democracy should really achieve, then the victim would at last get a word in sideways.

What became abundantly clear during my time at Parkhurst Prison was not only that murder was such a simple thing to do, homicide in some hands being almost a casual act – but that the victim was always the wrong person who happened to be in the wrong place at the wrong time. Of those murderers I got to know, the real target of the murderous assault was a parental figment, of precisely the sort to which so many of these pages have already been devoted.

So if we were interested in justice, we would pay attention to the victim. Why not a public compensation fund?   Why not have the offender repay? For a life taken, the compensation would be a regular annual payment, taken out of the offender's wage. We have life insurance against chance hazards, why not a similar arrangement for deliberate ones. For lesser damage, the compensation would be proportionately less.

But the offender would take responsibility, which is exactly what he or she assuredly should. The victim or his or her family would see this responsibility being discharged. Real people suffer real hardship. Real anti-social crimes injure real people – telling offenders they are scum and trash, and sweeping them under the carpet, helps no one – not them, not their victims, still less our society.

The criminal justice system is not good at prognosis – what it actually tries to do is 'retrognosis'. Prognosis attempts to establish what is likely to happen – retrognosis, what has already occurred. Not so much what he will do, but what he did. The medical profession has developed prognosis into a fine art – after all doctors have post-mortems to help refine their skills. The law is only slightly less proficient at retrognosis – it has as yet no equivalent audit.

Courts of law apply the only techniques they know, namely those which have proved fruitful in looking backwards in time. When applied to looking forwards, they cause problems.

Risk is assessable. If you know what caused an event, then you can count up the factors that still persist and thereby estimate how likely it is to recur. In this way, when you have your first heart attack, your clinicians can advise on the factors which led to it, and thereafter to the likelihood of your relapsing. Of course, if your psychiatrist turns his back on causative factors and retreats into the pea soup of 'bio-genetics' then her prognosis is likely to be as counterproductive as any judge's.

Much has been made on these pages of the concept of intent. Would you be surprised to learn that in assessing risk of recidivism, your average psychiatrist never asks what the prisoner intends to do?   Suppose a man has committed a horrendous crime. Not only does the conventional psychiatrist not ask why – he or she has not the slightest interest in finding out if you intend to do it again. This is one more disadvantage of excluding the notion of intent from today's psychiatry.

What passes for risk assessment today is more topsy-turvy than even Alice in Wonderland could devise. I have had a number of cases where the psychologist has taken pride in not asking the customer questions, but relying exclusively on what appears in writing, both in his or her medical or prison record, and in that new Holy Writ – 'the Literature'.

If you weren't born evil, then you have had it thrust upon you, such that you must remain locked away, interminably. Psychiatry's bankruptcy costs us all. The need for a better evaluation of emotions and of intent becomes pressing, a topic we now pursue in the closing part of this book.

Part Five –

Where we go from here

Part Five - Where We Go From Here

14 Science Versus Intent

Intent on Mischief • Ambitious Intentions • The Failure of Biosphere Two • Darwin's Omission • How Can Doctors Be so Certain? • Stable Knowledge • Sociably Sane

'All theory is against the existence of intent; all experience is for it'

[adapted from Dr Samuel Johnson]

Science is the search for Truth – it should therefore rally to the support of the first axiom described here. But the Truth about our intriguing world has proved utterly confusing. We are entitled to feel that Nature has let us down. We were doing so well at sorting out how the world worked. The electron rotated around the atom, in much the same way as the earth rotated round the sun. It seemed that the harder we worked and the more time and money we spent on scientific investigation, then the clearer and more understandable our world would become.

It was not to be. First the atom proved less and less like a miniature billiard ball, then time and space merged into a bewildering mish-mash. Instead of matter being fixed and solid, something we could safely munch our way through or walk upon – it could change, under odd circumstances, into a flash of light or other energy – $e = mc^2$. And then, as if to put the final nail in the coffin of our aspirations, at the very foundations of our world was Uncertainty – there was an agonizing trade-off between either knowing where a particle was, or where it was going, never both – no wonder the Uncertainty Principle is so little understood. In its essence it is incomprehensible, and always will be.

At the same time, though heavily muted by prodigious technological innovation, doubts were being voiced as to the reliability of theory, theory in general that is, first by David Hume in the 1740s, and lately by many others. Theory is meant to be 'what is really going on'. Theory is the simple principle on which all this confusion around us is meant to work. If you understand the theory, then you can eventually understand the world. At least that's the theory – in practice it doesn't work.

There are many reasons why theory is unreliable. As we saw with the Cuckoo Duck, too many factors are always going on already before we arrive on the scene. The presuppositions on which any theory is based are only ever partly fulfilled. You can never be sure that an effect which followed a cause yesterday will do so again today. You can in theory, but you cannot in practice.

There is no theory without thought, and every thought is a theory. If you put all your eggs in the 'science' or 'theory' basket, then these restrictions must be acknowledged if they are not to sink you. Thought is never as pristine as might appear, for as we discussed in the opening chapter, there is

238

no such thing as an emotionless thought, and emotions are intrinsically slippery.

In our everyday world we know that theory doesn't always work, it cannot be 100 per cent relied upon. We take it with a pinch of salt and muddle through as best we can. In theory, every time you turn the car's ignition key, the engine starts; in theory, every time you switch the computer on, it does what you expect; in theory, every time you take penicillin, the infection vanishes. But we don't rely 100 per cent on such theory – we take all theories as far as they will go, then we wing it, we 'suck it and see', we give them a fair chance and then we improvise. If we didn't, we'd be dead.

Intent on Mischief

In the past, there have been many different battles between belief systems. Science versus religion was the bane of Darwin's work. Today it is science versus intent. Just as God the Creator was incompatible with billions of years of evolutionary change, so today the notion that science can know everything is incompatible with personal choice or intent.

An illustration I rather like comes from mathematics. In theory 2 plus 2 equals 4 – always has, always will. Many take great comfort from the infinite range of mathematical theorems – they seem to offer a kind of idealism, a perfection that is singularly lacking from our real world. But mathematics has eventually to step down from its Olympian heights and re-enter the real world – and when it does, its pristine reliability falters. If 2 plus 2 equals 4 works in theory, how about practical reality? If you add 2 rabbits to 2 rabbits, the process is likely to involve multiplication not addition, and the result ends up as rather more than 4.

Now science would wish to check the validity of this proposition by controlled experiment, by double-blind trials, by weighing and measuring all parameters. All these methodologies would then confirm that adding 2 rabbits to 2 rabbits, can lead to millions – ask the Australians. So there can be no doubt that in reality, in experience, 2 plus 2 does not invariably equal 4. We would like it to, oftentimes it does, but you can never be 100 per cent sure it will. Of course there are provisos – the rabbits must be alive, they must be of mixed gender, they must have fodder – but it is precisely this sort of nitty-gritty detail that science is meant to float above. Here the presence of these mundane factors vanquishes the infallibility of the theory.

Nor is it just rabbits. Theory is supposed to predict. If you have the right theory, and a correct understanding of the data, then you should know what will happen next. Why bother with all those theoretical machinations if they don't have a beneficial impact on the real world we inhabit everyday? But suppose that the objects to which the theory applied decided they would do the opposite of what the theory predicted? Suppose they mischievously **chose** differently? Suppose they deliberately went out of their way to ensure that the outcome of your experiment was utterly different from what your theory had led you to expect? What would you do?

The temptation would be to say that the experiment would need to be done again with more compliant subjects. There would be tremendous pressure to preserve the theory in the face of experimental evidence against it – hardly the most propitious 'scientific' principle, and one with potentially disastrous consequences. Sacrificing the pursuit of Truth on the altar of preserving your earlier belief system is actually the antithesis of science.

Intent is incompatible with all theories about it – you cannot know something that has not yet been decided. You can blame the person who chooses, for being contrary and obstinate. You can even try and ignore the question entirely, saying that the sort of people who raise such issues are themselves notoriously unreliable.

But the difficulty is inescapable. Knowing things sits uneasily with allowing people to have a choice in the matter, an intent. If there are two or more ways a person can decide, you risk much by nailing your colours to the mast, saying that intent is imaginary. *'All theory is against the existence of intent; all experience is for it'.* Experience is actually more important than any theory, because that's the reality in which we live and die.

Ambitious Intentions

In the real world, intent is by no means problematic – we don't have serious misgivings about its existence. In fact, intent is highly valued, as indeed it should be. One of the major scientific projects envisaged for this new century is a trip to the planet Mars. What a splendid idea, all the technology appears now to be in place – all we need is a few billion dollars, euros or yen. But let's think back to our earlier great 'scientific project', the trip to the moon. What was John F. Kennedy doing when he committed the USA to go to the moon before the end of the 1960s? He was expressing an outrageous ambition, a highly inflated intention. How could he do this, if intent does not exist?

In theory, JFK was bound by chains of cause and effect stretching backwards into the mists of time. No one had ever seriously expressed the intention of going to the moon – there were many fictional, and wishful expressions, but none was backed by millions of dollars and by Congress. 'Unprecedented' is the word – something happened then which had never happened before. All theory states that Kennedy couldn't do what he actually did. His was a heroic act, but it was not unique. Other acts, some less, some more heroic, are committed on a regular basis. Human beings all over the place are conceiving entirely new intentions and then, believe it or not, putting them into operation.

And why should they not?   There is a curious schizophrenia abroad in the scientific community – great play is made for society's and taxpayers' support, but no allowance is made for the 'political will' by which alone this support can be delivered. It seems that intent is tolerated when it's needed, and downright excommunicated at all other times. Perhaps our academic institutions need to do some homework. For without intent, sanity and certainly Emotional Health, are entirely academic. However, when academe does put its collective weight behind the existence of intent, then our world would become that much safer.

The Failure of Biosphere Two

It is not quite true to say that all the technology is in place for a trip to Mars. Not to put too fine a point on it, what is still missing is a reliable understanding of the emotions. All astronauts can be coached to be physically fit – how many can be guaranteed to be Emotionally Healthy?   And we have a scientific experiment to prove just how disastrous emotional unfitness can be.

Biosphere Two was established in the 1990s, to simulate interplanetary travel. It was a sealed dome carefully stocked with state-of-the-art technology, in which, once sealed, nothing was allowed either in or out. Food was grown, waste recycled, the gaseous atmosphere was tightly controlled. And the emotions ran riot.

The outcome was not as predicted. Not only did a particularly nasty breed of ant begin to monopolize the micro-world, accompanied by an unpleasant rank weed – but the human inhabitants failed dismally to live up to expectations. They did not manage to live harmoniously together. They did not cooperate as their context required and as they had fully intended on entry. And their bickerings contributed to the failure of the mission. If this happens millions of miles from earth, escape will be less practicable. Emotions and the existence of intent make a material difference to human lives.

As they went in, the contestants assured all who would listen that they really wanted the project to succeed – their full intention was to make it a success. But emotions were not on the inventory. How could they be, when they are missing from academic science, just as they are missing from contemporary psychiatry? But if you miss them out, they tend to crop up anyway. And if you don't keep your eye on them, they will assuredly trip you up. If the project is a big one, its crises could be of equal size.

The intention of the contestants was clearly taken into account in the selection process of candidates for Biosphere Two, just as it will be for any putative Mars expedition. So despite intent being anathematized by contemporary scientists, it crops up when matters become important. The emotions do exactly the same. Perhaps the two axioms described earlier might assist such projects to curtail emotional storms.

Darwin's Omission

The written and spoken word allows us to do astonishing things. We can communicate with sages over many millennia, we stand on the shoulders of giants to attain yet greater insights. But, however much we achieve, we need to take care to note the obvious pitfalls which afflict our verbal abilities. This is especially important when discussing Emotional Health. Words can let us down rather badly. First of all, we need to acknowledge that both intent and the emotions exist. How can we do this when we cannot say with any precision at all what exactly either of them is? Can we sensibly discuss topics which are vague and indeterminate?

Does it make any sense to talk about things before defining the terms of our discussion?

There will be differing answers to these questions, largely dependent on the emotional confidence of the individual. If you are confident, and your discussants are people you can trust, then even though their terminology may be woolly, provided they can be relied upon to speak the Truth or as near as they can make it, and to intend responsibly, then we can make enormous progress, progress that is quite impossible without this umbrella of 'mutual understanding'. This is one further implication of the first axiom.

Take Darwin's 'abominable mystery' – how did the symbiosis between flowers and insects come about? This is something for which there is simply no sensible explanation. We simply do not know. We simply will never know. Spend 293 minutes watching *The Private Life of Plants*, the BBC television documentary by David Attenborough (see Appendix for details), and then ask yourself how is it possible for insects and other pollinating animals to develop such close coordination with plants. Bees pollinate flowers, as any visit to a summer garden will show. How did the bee know where to look? How did the plant know to produce not only pollen, which it needs for its own sexual reproduction, but also nectar, which it doesn't, except for bribing the bee? And as this astonishing documentary shows, it is not only nectar. There are packets of protein for ants, there are sexual pheromones for flightless wasps, there are visual images which so closely resemble what the insect is looking for as to leave you spellbound. The problems posed by the mysteries surrounding the Cuckoo Duck are chicken feed compared to these botanical spectaculars.

Now Darwin could provide no answer for this – it falls decidedly outside his terms of reference. His brief was to be as precise as possible, to define his terms as clearly as he could and develop a theory that was pristine, reliable and reproducible. All these epithets sound entirely admirable and would be heartily endorsed by every scientist before and since. But suppose there were some things which Darwin observed which required him to dip his pen into vague, indefinable terminology. What then? Suppose that a more accurate, more Truthful picture of what was going on required a certain elasticity in the terms deployed, a measure of licence to convey what rigid definitions cannot – could there be a legitimate 'scientific' use of poetic licence?

Darwin hints at this dilemma. In the Origin of Species he mentions the mistletoe, a plant which exists as we do, in one of two forms, either male or female. The mistletoe also has an astonishingly complicated mechanism for seed distribution. It coats its seeds with a sticky goo, such that after the bird has eaten some, it needs to wipe its beak vigorously to detach itself from the others, preferably (from the plant's viewpoint) lodging them firmly into the bark of another ash or apple tree altogether.

Darwin almost touches on an explanation, or partial explanation, which makes most sense to me out of an entirely dismal and murky set of alternatives. He goes out of his way to say that 'it is preposterous to account for the structure of this [plant] . . . by . . . the volition of the plant itself'. In other words, to suggest that the plant has even a modicum of 'intent' can be ruled out of consideration because it is a 'preposterous' suggestion.

But is it?

For one thing, if we came across a distribution system that was half as complex as the mistletoe's, but devised by a fellow human being, we would have no difficulty at all in supposing that it arose from ingenuity, from brilliant intent and forward planning. Or we would, if we were permitted to consider that humans had intentions. How else would we explain it? The number of techniques that have been devised to transmit not seeds, but binary digits in our ever expanding electronic era is breathtaking. The human imagination seems to know no limits in devising yet faster and more intriguing means of expressing and transmitting '1s', and '0s' all over the place. Without intents like these, our digital age would be stillborn.

The other, deeper reason for discounting Darwin's preposterousness is experience. *'All theory is against the existence of intent; all experience is for it.'* This aphorism advises giving more priority to experience. Not too much, but certainly more than Darwin, and many scientists feel immediately comfortable with. The point to emphasize here is that we can take certain liberties with words, and the definition of terminologies, provided always that we do so responsibly, that we keep as near the Truth as we can, and we acknowledge that trustworthy communications are at a premium. When we do this, we can communicate items which are vital for our wellbeing, even though at no time can we possibly define them in any rigid way whatsoever. The two concepts offered here on a strictly limited licence are first emotion and now intent. For if you once allow plants and insects to have intent, what can stop you allowing me to have it too, and vice versa?

How Can Doctors Be So Certain?

We yearn for verbal precision, just as we do for perfect knowledge. Both yearnings are entirely understandable, but when they lead to overlooking vitally important items, then we need to pause. A whole series of different philosophical approaches have based their search for Truth on the infallibility of words – linguistic analysis, logical positivism, reductionistic behaviourism – all may sound fine in theory, none work in practice. While recovering from a hefty dose of logical positivism which was all the fashion when I was studying philosophy at Cambridge, I was surprised to find that I was already being prescribed the antidote – clinical medicine.

Jemima was obviously very ill. She was feverish, listless and couldn't settle. Only 12 years old, she lolled around the bed in great distress. She hadn't eaten for a few days, she was becoming dehydrated, and her family, naturally enough, were very worried about her. What was going on? Come on, Doctor, for God's sake do something. This was not the ordinary cough and cold, this was not the standard throat infection. I had no idea what was happening. Worst of all, she was covered in angry red blotches. These were not your average skin rash – these meant business. They were all over her. They were uncomfortable, and to my horror, some of them were breaking down and coming up in sinister blisters. Clearly whatever it was had proved too much for the body's normal defences, and the skin had thrown in the towel and succumbed to blistering.

Normally in general practice the one thing you have plenty of is time – you can sit tight, await developments and then, when more evidence presents itself, you can see what it was that was going on at the start. When this isn't possible, then the family doctor is in a pickle – and clearly, with Jemima, time was of the essence. If I did not act, she might die. So, being a keen young general practitioner, I acted. As I repeatedly said to myself, I was not paid to worry – if I needed aid, I would get it. So I contacted the nearest paediatric unit, summoned the ambulance and dispatched Jemima to hospital as fast as the emergency services could manage.

The hospital doctor refused to admit her and sent her straight home. It was not some rare tropical disease, it was not galloping consumption. It was chickenpox. So why did I not know this? I had even suffered from exactly this disease myself, some 25 years earlier. How could it be that I did not know? The simple answer is that I had not, at that early stage in my family doctor career come across a case. It had not been in my experience. Certainly I had never seen a case in medical school – who in their right minds would ever send chickenpox sufferers to major teaching hospitals? So all the theory I had adsorbed was not sufficient to feed this simple, innocent diagnosis to me when I needed it.

The Truth is Jemima could have been suffering from smallpox – I have never seen a case of smallpox, so could not be 100 per cent certain. I would have reacted in exactly the same way had it been this dread plague – but I couldn't know, because I had no direct personal experience of it.

I expect most young doctors have similar anecdotes of their early learning experiences – but note what happened after that. As a family doctor, I saw more cases of chickenpox, of measles, of all the common diseases, than any ordinary member of the community. So when later I needed to argue the case against, say, a grandmother's dogma, I knew more than she, because I had seen more cases than she had. Later I repeatedly and entirely confidently made (or refused) the diagnosis of chickenpox or measles or whatever, and was able to reassure and calm the family's anxieties, because I knew more than all that family's experiences combined.

So experience does make a difference to how much you know. William Osler, my favourite clinician, was professor of medicine at Oxford University from 1905 to 1919. His aphorism *'Listen to the patient – s/he is telling you the diagnosis'* has saved my diagnostic bacon on a number of frantic occasions. His wisdom is especially relevant here. *'To see patients without books, is to go to sea without charts – but to read books without seeing patients is never to go to sea at all.'*

Clinical medicine proceeds under conditions which would be ruled entirely out of court were the standard definitions of academic science rigorously applied. For one thing its vocabulary consists essentially of terms such as 'health' and 'a normal pulse rate' – all of which are irredeemably amorphous and indefinable. For another, medical dogma proves decidedly unhealthy. Academic science on the other hand, holds its dogmatic views on the basis that the charts we have are (or will be) 100 per cent accurate, reliable and reproducible. The danger is that academic scientists will tend to restrict their fields of enquiry to those that do offer such precise charts. This is reminiscent of contemporary psychiatry, which rules out as 'not mentally ill' or 'untreatable' those customers who fail to appear on its charts.

The reality is that no chart can ever reflect 100 per cent the chaotic reality around us. This applies not only to clinical medicine, but to all aspects of any scientific enquiry anywhere. Sandbanks shift at sea, and basic scientific axioms crumble at an ever-increasing rate of knots. My prescription is to insist on responsible use of ill-defined terms, to apply as much Truth, Trust and Consent as can be summoned – and to proceed gingerly. When these conditions apply in medical practice, enormous therapeutic gains are possible. Without them, progress is problematic.

If you still insist that theory will win, that absolute and perfect charts will be available, then consider the following. We actually live moment to moment. I like the term 'existential moment', since this places due emphasis on the fact that we exist, at least we do at the moment of reading or writing. Perfect theory is needed to make perfect predictions. To show just how mysterious life is, place your finger on the pulse at your wrist. Can you predict when the next beat will come? Do you know anyone else who can? Few things are absolutely certain – but one such is that the time will come when it will beat no more.

After long experience and much reflection, I find myself saying – you have to know everything in the textbooks, to know that what you face today isn't in them. Expressing this in Osler's splendid chart metaphor – you need to know what all the charts say, so you can plot a better course when they run out. All medical practitioners and all engineers do this from time to time – innovators do it all the time. So fluid and fickle are emotional diseases that you can virtually guarantee that yesterday's chart doesn't apply – it is already out of date. What a challenge. But what it does do is place due emphasis on the unique value of experience. And when it works, as it generally does nowadays, it's wonderful. Such skills are life-saving – sad they fade with age.

The ignorances in clinical medicine are profound. And for all our modern technology will assuredly remain so. But that does not mean we give up. It means we prioritize. When treating a medical customer for the first time, I do not expect to learn everything at once. But there are certain essentials I need to know first. I have precisely four minutes to tell if he or she is breathing adequately. If I don't make this my first priority, my other ignorances will have less relevance in five minutes time.

Experience teaches you these priorities. It is impossible to know everything – it is entirely possible to know enough to do more good than harm. And the priorities we need to adopt in pursuing Emotional Health are given in the two axioms described here. It is also essential that we give weight to the inexplicable notion that both emotion and intent exist – for by doing that, we can gain not only better Emotional Health, but also longer lives.

Stable Knowledge

Stability of knowledge falls into the same packet as emotional stability. We need our fellow humans to confirm or deny the relative Truth of our transient dogmas. By jointly seeking what is real, and by communicating that between ourselves, we can in fact generate a real stability of which theoreticians can only dream. Of course, deceit, distrust and coercion can soon put a stop to this particular avenue of relief – but when human beings are behaving humanely, then stability of our view of the world can indeed be ensured, at least enough to assist our surviving longer in it than otherwise.

The two axioms offered here do not carry the authority of scientific proof. If we once eschew coercion, then scientific coercion must also loose its stranglehold – these axioms then gain credence by persuasion, or not at all – these are things you have to work out for yourself. These are not proofs but offerings, a bit like my favourite recipes. They rely on each individual customer trying every one of them out for themselves, in their own time and at their own pace. They may not be True, you may not be able to Trust them – and on no account whatsoever, should you accept them without your full hearted Consent to do so.

But then this is hardly new. Ever since we were born, we have been offered various views of the curious world into which we so precipitously arrive – not all of which prove to have long term validity. Sorting sensible sheep from egregious goats is a sure sign of Emotional Health.

Imagine a ping-pong ball floating atop a water fountain. It is held there by upward pressure from below. The water is never the same, it keeps rushing past, with endless motion. It is the motion that keeps the ball aloft. The ball is defying gravity, another intractable law of physics. The energy input which permits this defiance comes from the water pressure itself.

Take this picture into the field of human mental activity. Here the pressure, the motion, comes from intent, and emotion. Here the items of our mental furniture that float so dramatically and defiantly are notions and flights of imagination. And the wonder they induce and emote is a constant source of delight – each one of us has the power of the imagination, the ability to intend – and if we deploy it, and practise it long and hard enough, the creativity we can harness will need to be seen to be believed.

Wouldn't it be sad, to suppose from first principles that we were just too rigid to notice the difference between living and non-living processes? Just because water can never run uphill, it does not follow that living organisms must always be equally in thrall to gravity. Open your eyes on a hot summer day, and actually see just how remarkable it is that zillions of insects and other aerial animals defy gravity with breathtaking exuberance. Science has taught us a great deal – we burn fewer witches these days. But inflexibility exacts a fearsome penalty in the evolutionary stakes – if we cannot inch open our perceptions to admit intent into our discussions, then such ignorance costs more than we think. If we can, then we all become that little bit more alive. Could be fun.

Sociably Sane

When the mind goes wrong, it does so because it is being driven not by one, but by two intents, at the same time. One intent is pushing one way, and the other, the other. This is not a thin distinction, indeed it is difficult to overlook – unless that is precisely what the victim desperately intends. The two intents relate to infant and adult survival strategies.

Those who deny we have any possibility of intent in the first place, by this very decision exclude themselves from any understanding of the painful agonies of mental disease. Their intransigence prevents them being of any help. Without acknowledging intent, there can be no possibility of either assessing nor assisting sanity (let alone participating in it).

Continuation of infantile survival strategies into adult life causes many problems, as we have seen. Worse, some adults retain an unthought-through fondness for the certainties of the kindergarten, a persistence of the notion that there is a world that larger people know about, and control – and if only we can get there, we too will be saved. For some, 'science' offers this figmentary ideal. The harsh Truth is that such an infantile reality has gone for ever. In adulthood there is no one 'out there' to rescue us, or who knows 'everything'. If we do not take responsibility for ourselves – we will meet the consequences of all irresponsibilities, namely sliding gracelessly ever nearer death and extinction.

The converse is also true. If we can once throw in our lot with those we actually have around us today, with the actual human beings we meet, get to know, and grow fond of – why then we have a key to sorting out these horrendous philosophical headaches.

Get the people we know to give us a lift with our overgrown mental furniture, inveigle our fellows to lend their stout shoulders to our mutual emotional support, persuade them that together we can all become ever more sociably sane. Now there's a prospect that would gladden the heart of any puzzled enquirer, it would resolve the 'indelible ignorance' issue, and if we can once deploy the two axioms described, then it would bring within our grasp for the first time that acme of all consciousness – peace of mind.

15 Society's Struggles with Serfs

Serfs – a Legal View • An Avoidable Serf • Stopping Serfs at Source • Poverty Breeds Serfs – a Public Health Issue • Coercion and Emotional Neotony • Future Creativities

Emotional Health applies as much to societies as to individuals. Just as it is entirely appropriate to aim to become a fit, healthy, stable adult – so too every society should aspire to take a delight in itself and become a delightful place in which to live. In this new century we need to discard the fundamentally dismal picture of human beings so prevalent in the last, and apply the prescription for Emotional Health on a wider, global scale.

There is a close parallel between emotional maturation, to which so much space has been devoted here, and the development over the last few centuries of our modern quasi-democratic societies. In the recent past the feudal baron was a father figure, and his dependants hung on his every word like infants in a kindergarten. His word was law – nothing happened without his sanction. There are families and other societies still like this, where the parent is still the sovereign ruler, though happily fewer than there were.

The remedy is to apply to wider societies the rule which parents often find so challenging at home. The need to bring the child up, and bring the child up to be independent, is just as crucial for maintaining a mature society as it is for any family. Every citizen needs to become ever more independent and autonomous, and have decisions devolved down from governing parent-figures to his or her level, as of right. This devolution calls for constant, careful and energetic intervention to ensure it progresses healthily.

This is simply the parental dilemma we met in an earlier chapter writ large. We have global responsibilities which, if we do not discharge them adequately, will land us with global costs. If we get this parental dilemma wrong, our dependants do not just fall over – they go to war, nowadays globally.

Serfs – A Legal View

The law divides everyone into two flavours – infants and adults. If you are under 18 you are the one, if over, the other. The changeover comes automatically, merely with the passage of time – you don't have to ask anyone's permission, nor fulfil any particular qualification or test – just sit there and grow up. This is reassuring – the law makes no distinction on the grounds of skin colour, sex, sexual orientation, power, size, weight, height, wealth, origin, birth, religion, moral persuasion, or even of age, apart from this. And if the law doesn't, then neither should we.

Unhappily, human beings can be contrary – so in practice a third category is called for. Hopefully this will be temporary, since, of course, it can have no basis in law – though in view of our rampant emotional confusions, its elimination may take some time. If adults insist on behaving as infants, or others regularly treat them as such, then the technical term I suggest is 'serf'.

It's really a question of who is in charge. If you are, then you are autonomous, responsible and adult. If you are not, then you are dependent, others are responsible for you and you are infantile. Of course, as we have discussed at some length, if you are under age, then there is nothing wrong with being dependent – indeed parenting is essential to keep you alive. The troubles begin if you are of age – and still insist on being underaged. Or others do so on your behalf. Then you are a serf.

We need to re-examine how our social structures struggle to discourage serfs. For obviously if we really are all born Lovable, Sociable and Non-violent, and we all thrive on adequate supplies of Truth, Trust and Consent – then this could usefully be reflected in our everyday institutions. If we believed these axioms implicitly, we would see to it that they are. The pathway to Emotional Health is shown by the individual becoming ever less serf-like. On the wider social scale, Emotional Health entails promoting ever-increasing autonomy and self-confidence globally, working energetically and continuously towards reducing the global number of serfs to zero.

Perhaps the most manifestly irrational of all our social institutions are our prisons. Our penal policies encourage precisely the things we ostensibly wish to eliminate. Clearly we need to lock mad axemen away, so that they cannot continue to slaughter us. Nothing wrong with that. But if our aim is to stop them mangling us, we need to do rather more. We need to find out why they did it, so as to know what needs to change, so that they stop. We would much prefer them to be solid, stable, supportive citizens, contributing to the general weal, rather than undermining it. The best way to achieve this is to persuade them that they are adults. The last thing to do is confirm in their minds that they are not in charge, they are not responsible, they are not autonomous.

Prisons breed serfs, at great and increasing cost – a cost paid by their clientele, their staff and by our wider society. Let's take a look at Jim.

An Avoidable Serf

Jim was 29 and a little overweight when I first met him in Parkhurst Prison. He was limited by lack of education, but he had a gentle sense of humour when he felt relaxed, which he did infrequently. He had, how can I put this delicately? – difficulties with his personal hygiene. He could also be quite awkward at times, and not a little devious. Hardly had I arrived in the prison, than he registered an official complaint against me (the only one I ever had) to the Regional Prison Medical Officer, complaining bitterly about my treatment. He objected as fiercely as he could to my 'forcing him to accept treatment'. This was not a very encouraging thing for him to do to me, but then he was altogether a rather discouraged individual. I assured the Medical Officer that Jim could get up and leave my office any time he wished – and when I next got the chance, I made exactly this point to Jim himself. I tried to explain that Consent was one of my fundamental tenets. Jim grunted – he had other fish to fry.

After that, Jim would exercise this right to leave at the drop of a hat, and walked out of my office on a regular basis. He would leave after a minute, after five, or, if feeling particularly indulgent, after ten. The timing varied, but was never extensive. He would sometimes allow me to videotape our sessions, but mostly not – he was asserting his arbitrary control wherever he could. I therefore realized that if I wished to make any progress I would have to grasp those opportunities that Jim somewhat inadvertently allowed me. So on one such occasion, I braced myself and declared in as matter of fact a tone as I could manage – 'Jim, you think you are garbage, don't you?' To which Jim had no difficulty in replying that he did. I then embarked on one of those 'surprise' twists described in earlier chapters. I said, equally firmly and without making any big issue of it – 'I don't think you're garbage'.

Here was I trying to be positive. This was affirmative action. It was a disaster. Jim glared, and fled. He refused to talk to me, even to acknowledge me for a month or more. He broke off diplomatic relations, and our conversations were at an end. What had I done? He and I were now incommunicado. How could it be that a seemingly innocent remark had produced such an adverse reaction? It was abundantly obvious, even in an olfactory sense, that Jim had a drastically low opinion of himself – but why react like a scalded cat when I suggested that there might be an alternative view? In terms of the second axiom, how could he ever regard himself as Lovable, if even the first step in this direction precipitated such an outburst?

Some time after Jim and I had reached this conversational impasse, I was being interviewed on the local radio about handling violence and curing psychopaths. I discussed a number of issues and then mentioned Jim, though without spelling out his name. I described how some of the prisoners were so low in their own estimation that it was difficult to reach down and give them a lift. I mentioned that one had even cut off all communications for the single reason that I had told him I did not think he was garbage. The interviewer nodded, and moved on to other matters.

Imagine my surprise when Jim next agreed to see me, to find him eyeing me knowingly, saying, 'That was me you were talking about, wasn't it?'   He had heard the radio interview, and immediately recognized himself in it. He gave a little smile. Though I had failed to make contact with him face to face, I had managed to reach him via the radio waves – whoever said human beings were straightforward. He started pulling himself round. He discovered soap. He still declined to engage in direct Emotional Education, he still insisted on being peripheral – but his confidence in himself began to grow.

He came from a large, impoverished family, was routinely neglected, both in and out of school. His schooling was disastrous, effectively sealing his fate. He would brat about at the back of the class, broke into deserted factories for something to do and learned remarkably little. Unsurprisingly, his vocabulary was limited – when I mentioned to him that his self-esteem was low, he retorted sharply that there was nothing wrong with his 'steam'. Ah, the joys of being literate.

His crime was murder, for which he was serving a life sentence. As I relate his story now, it occurs to me just how this murder really happened. He did not have enough rage within to drive him to premeditated murder with criminal intent – he was a drifter more than a doer, he was too incompetent to achieve whatever he planned. And the person who died was a girlfriend, whom he had abruptly pushed away. On falling backwards, this friend struck her head, cracked her skull and died. What had happened, it now occurs to me, is that she had said something similar to my remark – she had told Jim she liked him, or that he was not garbage to her. He was totally unable to accommodate this. In pushing her away he triggered a course of action which led to even such little self-esteem as he did have, being leached away from him by our irrational punitive society. Sadly, our esteemed criminal justice system had neither the delicacy nor the interest in uncovering the real Truth behind the homicide.

How much is society responsible for Jim's crime?   And what have we done to repair the damage and prevent it recurring? Poverty in a material sense certainly contributed. But emotional poverty was even more damaging. Note too that the damage Jim inflicted arose from the experiences he had had. He was not a self-sufficient, mature adult. He had never established himself as one. He had so little control over his environment, so little 'self-reliance', so little Trust in his fellows, that even the most benign remark precipitated mayhem. In other words, he had been brought up a serf, and as such he represented a hazard to the rest of society. It has not helped that, at great expense, society has thoroughly cemented his appallingly low self-esteem. Serfs cost us all.

Stopping Serfs at Source

I know from my work that if you can build a trusting therapeutic relationship, then the irrational and emotionally confused individual will Consent to perceive the painful yet healthier Truth of their situation. Let's look at a social project that worked brilliantly, which shows how such an approach works equally well on the wider social scale.

The High Scope Project began in the 1960s, in Ypsilanti, a town near Detroit, Michigan in the United States. The project took 123 children aged three and four, from African-American families and gave them, for around 18 months, what I would describe as 'super-play-school'. The motto was 'self-reliance' – something that both Jim and Larry earlier, signally and lethally lacked. All serfs do. The key components were involving the child in deciding what activities he or she would engage in on that day, and enrolling the active interest of the parents in the child's progress. These were poor children from a black ghetto facing the vicious downward cycle of the poverty trap.

The children were divided into two groups, employing a highly sophisticated research methodology. The non-program group was carefully matched with the program group, and acted as a 'control' to ensure that any difference was attributable to the project rather than to chance. When the children reached the age of 27, the results were astonishing. Four times as many in the program group were earning $2000 a month or more. This group had five times fewer arrests, and five times as many girls married as compared with the non-program group.

'Over the life time of the participants, the pre-school program returns to the public an estimated $7.16 for every dollar invested.' Not only should we invest heavily in child care and education because we are a civilized society and they represent our future, but as this project makes abundantly clear, it pays us handsomely in cash terms to do so. It is time that some of these basic human principles were reinjected into our political debate, and that we ensured that our administrators took note of our more benign intentions.

The two features of this project which most appeal to me are the involvement of the parents and the eliciting of the child's Consent. I picture the impact on the child somewhat as follows. For a brief glimpse, for some 18 months on average, the children experience an environment in which parents are encouraged to participate in their lives and in which their intentions are respected – what they want, chose or intend is seen to matter. Thus when the grim tide of poverty closes over them again, they have stored within, a picture of something better, something where they do matter, where people do take notice of them, and they can gain benefit from behaving responsibly and obtain feedback from being Sociable. In a sense, in the micro-society we ran in Parkhurst Prison, these were also our objectives – and our success in implementing them was reflected as here, with lower crime, lower violence and a determination and a newly discovered intent to behave more sociably and more responsibly in future.

Look at the figures for marital relationships. Our current marital decay rate is frightening – here we have a technique which impacts precisely on that destructive tendency. I would also confidently predict fewer mental diseases including schizophrenia and other psychoses as a result of this project, though I failed to elicit the Director's agreement on this point – he is an admirably cautious man. How can we let this knowledge gather dust on the shelf? Where are the changes that need to guarantee that these insights are implemented not only in pre-school groups, but throughout our society?

For that is the next step. Where we go from here is to take
our social institutions by the scruff of the neck and 'persuade'
them with some energy into healthier, less irrational
channels. The High Scope Project catered for children aged 3
and 4. What about those aged 0 to 2, or 5 to 85 or nowadays
105? Every one can benefit from having their Consent
elicited and their immediate emotional support networks
spruced up – so why not take active steps along these lines
now?

Poverty Breeds Serfs – A Public Health Issue

Poverty as mentioned, is a major social disease. It calls
urgently for a public health campaign. From poverty, and its
associated stress, come legions of disabilities. These
disabilities poison all societies, most obviously via the
infections, enteric diseases such as cholera, tuberculosis,
AIDS and so forth, all of which flourish in slum conditions and
are ever ready to break out and pounce on us all, in pandemic
proportions.

More important for a rich world is the risk that poverty poses
to social anarchy, from which, on this small planet, none of us
can escape. The poor and deprived have no investment in a
stable, prosperous society any more than Jim did – time we
gave them one. If our global society crashes, as it has in the
past and risks doing so again, the poor have little to lose –
time we gave them more.

Poverty afflicts all groups, both in our local societies and
across the globe. And its remedy is blindingly simple – enskill
the pauper and buy her product.

The disease of poverty is not primarily the absence of cash –
though this is its most striking symptom. It is the absence of
earning ability. It is the absence of self-confidence, it is the
lack of social and other skills to engage in gainful social

interchange with other members of our diverse species. In a nutshell, poverty breeds serfs.

Globally, rich countries owe it to themselves to remedy the poverty of the remainder. Serfs impose the most crippling social costs, and if we do not curtail them, we can all of us confidently expect to suffer severe social damage as a direct result. It is only a matter of time – is there enough left? It is not too far-fetched to suppose that every global trouble spot in the world today, every guerrilla war, is driven essentially by poverty and the excess of serfs which this disease breeds.

Without doubt it was the sudden, unexpected attack of the poverty disease in Germany in the early 1930s that proved such a shock to the body politic. Like acute stress in an individual that can paradoxically lower the protective immune system, and allow a virus strike to succeed – so too, the poverty shock allowed Hitler his initial electoral success in 1932 without which he would have remained a mere rabble-rouser, as Sir Oswald Mosley did. We don't need SWAT teams, we need Emergency Enskilling Teams. If we can afford to spend such a high proportion of our national wealth on 'defence', we can afford to spend a tenth on 'poverty and serf empowerment' – it is all a matter of emotional attitudes, and indeed of global Emotional Health. And in economic terms war costs most.

Poverty is an economic disease, and the economic remedy is obvious – trade, both micro and macro. At the present time financial aid given to poor nations is running at something like a tenth the value of the trade which would be possible, were all irrational embargoes lifted. Wealthy pressure groups, with easy access to the levers of political power, impose irrational tariffs and too many other irresponsible obstacles.

What is required is not so much philanthropy, not the goodness of your heart, but hard economic sense. The rich need to become better, less irrational business(wo)men, then both rich and poor will benefit. Short-term discrimination against paupers maintains the disease. Why not expand the economically active population? In that way the market for our goods and services also grows. Ergo, enlarge economic activity by all sensible means available. If this requires a minuscule level of pump priming, then let's have a low-level tax, and invest it world-wide, thus reaping globally economic and social returns similar to those enjoyed by the High Scope Project. We pay for life insurance – how about global social insurance? The premiums are astonishingly low, though it does require a change in prejudices and an adequate supply of Emotional Health. This is not going to be easy, since some prejudices are learnt deep – especially when we are very, very young.

Coercion and Emotional Neotony

All human babies are small, light in weight and easily portable. You can pick one up with little or no effort, and put them wherever you fancy. In fact the degree of control that you can exercise over any one of these micro-human beings is deeply seductive. When we too were growing up, we soon learnt that bigger children can bully us with impunity, when the teacher isn't looking, so when later we meet those who happen to be smaller or weaker, we are quick to take steps to ensure they do not do the same. If we are insecure, we find it hard to change and keep taking these same steps so as to preserve ourselves – we try never to let these potential hostiles gain an advantage over us – keep them small, powerless and under control.

The harder these survival strategies are learnt, the more difficult are they to shift. So those weaker are seen as controllable – and too often we move to keep them that way, permanently. We learn to look to bigger people, larger agents, richer patrons, higher authorities, to protect us, ignoring the fact that our infantile reality has now changed – in adulthood different factors apply.

In evolutionary terms, preserving infantile patterns into adulthood is known as neotony. Thus a tadpole which retains its infantile tail grows not into a frog, but a newt. In Homo sapiens, this emotional neotony threatens to prove our fatal evolutionary flaw, inching us towards extinction, most likely via thermonuclear irradiation.

Nothing else is required to explain why we slaughter ourselves so regularly with ever more elaborate weaponry – we are stuck in childhood. We still believe that others are in charge, that bigger, more powerful people will betray us, and that those around are just as unreliable as ever they were when we were 100 per cent dependent.

Our ancestors lost all their fur because it impeded their swimming, and then moved back on to land, where water no longer floated their infants. As neonates we can float beautifully, we can grip tight to parental hair, with no problem, within minutes of birth. But being now terrestrial, we are entirely dependent for our physical location on the reliability of adults – some of whom are more preoccupied than others. Traumas or fears of being dropped would not have occurred had we been born into a watery environment – have we enough evolutionary time left, to develop and then adapt to, a reliably supportive Sociable strategy? Can we learn fast enough to counteract our emotional neotony – which is where serfs come from?

Future Creativities

The reality is that we are a society of living organisms. And now a unitary global society. So we need to find out for ourselves if we really are capable of being Trusted, whether we can actually distinguish Truth from deceit – and having done so, whether or not we will Consent to live peaceably together, like adult citizens.

Then we will find, as a society, that life is more secure, more enjoyable and longer. At least that is a clear prescription. The more you feel in charge, and the less you feel a serf – the more stable you become. And so it is for our society – as we all feel more confident, self-reliant, adult and secure, then that's how our future will be.

By reinstating the primacy of intent, we can give credence to the splendours of which the human mind is capable. If we can intend, then we can organize. If we can organize, then we can create. And if we can create, what limits are there to our creativity?

Being creative and being Lovable all come in the same package. The more creative you are, then the more interest you will prove to be to those who matter to you. If you are a dab hand at rustling up novel dishes in the kitchen, then you will never want for a meal companion. If you can whistle a merry tune, or pipe a splendid roundelay, or any other creative performance – then you are confirming to those around that you are a Sociable animal, and contact with you, and you with them, enhances all – a gain in productivity akin to the infinitely divisible 'mental loaf' described earlier.

Being a serf, or tolerating them on the premises or anywhere else in our global society, carries a high risk and a heavy penalty. Emotional Health, however, provides a sure and certain remedy, whenever required. Adults do differ from infants – and the more who see this for the fact that it is, the better. You never can tell beforehand which serf has the vital skill to save your, or your loved one's, life. The only reliable remedy is actively to promote all serfs to full adulthood – and the sooner the better – that way we all become that much safer.

Before this final chapter closes, here's a further vignette, to illustrate just how vital Emotional Health is for us all. The difficulty Freud had in escaping his childhood traumas has been highlighted, together with the unhappy legacy he left us all as a result. The other key witness to our current view of ourselves is Darwin – did he suffer diminished self-confidence, was he less Emotionally Healthy than he might have been?   What would he have said, had he been more confident?   For though it might not seem immediately obvious – your level of Emotional Health does determine how you see and react to the world.

Returning to Darwin's omission, what he called his 'abominable mystery' – let's look at a practical sample. There is a black flightless wasp shown in Attenborough's television documentary mentioned in the previous chapter, which, since she generally lives below ground, has use for neither colour nor wings. Such immobility has its limitations when she wishes to mate. Her resolution of her reproductive problem is itself quite astonishing – and quite impossible even to contemplate in the utter absence of a minuscule amount of 'intent'. How could you invent such a strategy?   The documentary shows her climbing to the top of a grass stalk, where she proceeds to emit a minute quantity of scent. This wafts downwind and attracts males of her species, who fly to her, land on her back, whisk her away in the best Arabian tradition, mate with her and then release her back to continue her quotidian subterranean life.

How does she know?   She has never seen a grass stalk in her life before – why climb to the top?   How long did it take to synthesize the correct chemical pheromone which males of her species would first recognize and then react to? Suggestions that there are legions of flightless wasps whose pheromonic chemistry was one pip out, such that they attracted males of the wrong species or none at all – such suggestions do not sit well with the sophistication and precision shown by all living organisms in successfully organizing themselves and their sexual and social relations. This is not trial and error, random stabs in the dark – this is something far more akin to mini-intent – at least it is for my money.

But we are not even halfway through. Attenborough's documentary was about plants, not exotic insects. Though it is impossible to conceive how the wasp arrived at her precise sexual machinations, there are far deeper mysteries to come. The documentary shows a plant mimicking the wasp. Think about that sentence, a plant imitating an insect. We humans have enough trouble grasping what the wasp gets up to – we cannot smell the pheromone, but at least we have eyes to see the wasps' behaviour. The plant has no sense organs whatsoever that can assist its 'understanding' of an animal. It cannot see, hear, smell, touch nor taste its symbiotic ally – how on earth can it imitate it?

The plant grows a flower that looks adequately like a female wasp on the end of a stalk. It then emits a pheromone exactly as does the female wasp herself. The plant does not need the female, and has never 'seen' one. The botanical pheromone is precisely on target – it matches the wasp's down to a tee. What is going on here? If you don't feel a little weak at the knees, perhaps you should.

The male wasp attracted by the imitation pheromone lands on the mimicked female and attempts to fly off with her. The plant has already 'worked out' that this is what was about to happen, and has evolved or grown a 'hinge' which allows the flower head to bounce up, and so arrange for the back of the male to be covered in pollen. Where did this precision of coordination come from? How did the information, let alone the strategy, get into the plant's genome?

The emotive word Darwin had for this was negative – 'abominable'. This was because he didn't like mysteries. His task was to eliminate the mysterious by ploughing forwards with precise and exact terminologies. He worked out many aspects of the astonishing biologic variety around, and he was annoyed that he could not take the matter forward.

Coming at this challenge in the twenty-first century, we are free to substitute a different word – 'awesome', 'fascinating', 'inspiring' are now available, for those confident enough to view the world from a stable, Emotionally Healthy base. We need to accept that we can never know everything – indeed we can never know very much at all. This ignorance is permanent, it is indelible. It is not 'abominable' if we can once appreciate that we can know enough to make a benign difference. But to do this, we need to overcome our hazardous prolonged childhoods – but then that is what Emotional Health is all about, both individually and globally.

Once we achieve a degree of emotional stability, these awe-inspiring manifestations of life's creativity can be seen as a source of wonder and delight. They can help stimulate our creative and imaginative natures, prod us to develop our own capacities for organizing ourselves and our societies responsibly, and in a beautiful, delightful manner. The incredible mysteries which so undermined Darwin's peace of mind can, if we are secure enough emotionally, serve to re-evaluate our real position and encourage us to seek out ever more sources of imperishable delights – a worthy extension of the quest for Emotional Health.

Can we live happily ever after, in our newly global society? We can assuredly live a great deal more happily, both individually and globally, if we see more clearly what is around us, and indeed where the emotions inside us come from. We can also create a great deal more delight if we learn more thoroughly what our fellows are really like and what 'being alive' really means – not what we presumed, or 'have always known', them to be. The challenge is to grasp as firmly as possible the crucial and imperishable values of Truth, Trust and Consent and use them to determine as clearly as we can whether or not we are all born Lovable, Sociable and Non-violent – for if we do, and if we are, then both peace of mind and peaceful global societies are within our grasp.

Poverty breeds serfs, but serfs breed war. Just as in the absence of the smallpox virus, there can be no smallpox disease – so without serfs, war is impossible. Eliminate all serfdom and you eliminate all wars. Now there is a new millennial prize worth having – a golden cure for warfare. What do you say to that?

Appendix

Appendix

This appendix contains four items, widely varied in origin and content – some will appeal to some readers, others to others – it is unlikely all will appeal to all. However, since this is the first opportunity I have of publishing this material, I have taken full advantage of my editorial prerogative to include them all. My advice would be to read those that are of interest, and skip the rest.

Firstly then, a letter recently received from Charlie Bronson. Charlie is widely thought of as the most dangerous prisoner in the British prison system. In fact through my personal contacts with him, I have always found him quite straightforward, and very much less dangerous than many others. His violence is directed mostly at inanimate objects, and has certainly never been used to kill anyone.

In a recent television programme, I pointed out that his case represents a conspicuous failure of current penal policy. After an inept bank robbery, in which no one was killed, he has so far spent 26 years in prison. Far from assisting our citizens to lead a sensible, adult life, our present criminal justice system here contrives to spend around £2,000,000 making an unfortunate man worse.

Prisoners in this country are not allowed to change their name by deed poll. So Charlie re-named himself while on one of his brief sojourns in the community, when he was legally permitted to adopt the name of his then favourite film star.

I include his letter here to show how a long-experienced prisoner views my work. Over the years since our first encounter on 5th July 1991, Charlie has regularly written to me – pleading with me to treat him. The Home Office blankly refuses. They regard him as one of their most difficult challenges. Yet despite having no idea what to do with him themselves, they consistently obstruct my expertise. Is there a legal case concerning Charlie's legitimate quest for medical treatment of his own choice?

The television documentary by David Attenborough referred to earlier, is 'The Private Life of Plants' BBCV 5528, originally transmitted 5th January – 9th February 1995. It is 293 minutes long. It's IPC reference is – 5-014503- 552824 >.

Next in this appendix, are four poems by Kate Holden. I include them since they describe how the points made in the book impacted on her personal experience.

Following these, is a paper I wrote after discussions with the Editor of the Lancet regarding the present difficulties in which psychiatric now finds itself.   He declined to print it.   I include it here to give chapter and verse to the arguments which appear above. It is likely to be too technical for some readers, but I include here for completeness.

Finally is a letter that was published in the Lancet.

Letter from Alice Miller

June 4, 2002

Dear Bob,

Thank you for having sent me your book, To me, it is very inspiring and true. I absolutely agree with you that people need to trust their enlightened witness to be able to face and bear their truth and that this can't be done without consent. But to go into such a process is, as you rightly say, the last thing a person wants to do. So I am wondering how you get your patients to trust you and try with you despite their reluctance. I suspect that it is your confidence in the power of the truth that ensures the successful outcome.

I would also very much appreciate to learn more about the details of the stories you mention in your book: why are these people in prison, what did they do to deserve this outcome, what happened to them in childhood and how do they see today their parents? Maybe you will offer this material in one of your next books, I

Your book rings so right to me because I have no doubt about the fact that acknowledging the truth stored up in our body, acknowledging it by our emotions and our mind is exactly what we need to become healthy. What you do is (in my understanding) to make people aware of their hidden agendas, to wake up their curiosity and to enable them to use their logical thinking of the adult person they now are. By dropping the irrational contradictory way of thinking they can liberate themselves from the compulsion to repeat. As children under terror they couldn't do that. Their thinking was disturbed by fear.

Unfortunately, there are not yet many psychiatrists who could agree with us. But things are going to change, hopefully soon.

With best wishes for your work that will certainly help many to eventually come out of their inner emotional prison which keeps them for years in a state they no longer should be in. Then, they become able to live freely and responsibly.

Alice Miller

Letter from Charlie Bronson

To Dr Bob Johnson

What amazed me is this! All your good work as C-Wing psychiatrist, and what do they do ... "close it" and sling you out.

No place ever in the British penal system had such a success as C-Wing. And they just close it!

F*** the inmates. Put them back in the dungeons! Many have actually died Bob. All have got worse.

> Big 'A B' – a mystery – died
> 'C D' – dead
> 'E F' – dead

We are all dying slowly. Few if any have made it Bob. The only one I believe is doing well is 'G H' in 'X' prison.

The rest are scattered all over the dungeons. Many are here, or up in 'Y' prison.

That Michael Howard has a lot to answer for! "Me" – I just seem to exist.

A year has flown by in this cell. No bed. No window. No toilet lid or seat. Total isolation.

They call it a progressive system!

It's shit, Bob. False and evil. This place has a psychologist. (Not <u>one</u> has even come to my door). They're just hypocrites.

Anyway

Like the cartoon –

    I'm hanging about –

        treading time.

            Waiting – Preparing

One day it will crack open and some Truth will seep out.

Charles Bronson April 2000

      ɞ   ø   ɞ   ø

Charlie read through this book and his single comment was, "awesome book", and he passed it on to his mates.

      ɞ   ø   ɞ   ø

Dear Bob, These are some poems

Looking forward to seeing you on Sunday. These are some poems I wrote in hospital - I hope you enjoy them !

Love Katie Holden [aged 14]

Let me in
Let me see what you see
Let me think what you think
Show me the way, light my path
I'll do anything if you let me in
To your secret world
Where are you?
I'm searching
My eyes can still look
Even though my mind doesn't think.
If you protect me now,
I'll protect you in years to come.
If you remember me now,
I'll never let you fade.
Don't let me waste my life - jump
in, come on inside,
I'll let you in.

Even the deepest, darkest ocean floors,
Far from life, just worlds of shadowed sand,
Even they see light, reflected onto the decaying plants,
Just for a moment the windows are opened and light pours in,
Reaches out and grasps at every corner,
Filling the bed in floods of colour,
And then it vanishes and the windows are closed.
Even the deepest, darkest thoughts,
So obviously wrong in other's eyes,
Even they see light and hope and love,
Someone can open the windows, shut for so long,

And the world seems so clear and unaffected,
So full of life,
But then the light disappears and those same thoughts reappear.
Is it so hard to keep the light on?
Open the windows, and take a look,
The outside world is waiting,
I'm ready to face it and keep going,
The light manages to shine through even these prison walls,
And I couldn't have reached where I am,
Without you.

12/2/00
I'm searching for a explanation, some reason for my pain,
My once shut eyes re-open, now I'm outside looking in.
I've run down the same cobbled path for way too long,
I've reached the edge and carried on,
I only realise the damage that I've done,
Others have suffered beneath my selfish, thoughtless self
It's time to change, turn back and find the Truth.
I have a long road ahead, and I'll walk slowly
Back the way I came until I find my spirit waiting,
Where I left it when I began this troubled journey
So long ago, for so many reasons.
When I finally reach the end, at least I can say,
I've passed the cross roads and survived,
Jumped the cliff and found a ledge,
And it's only showed my strength and courage that
If I conquer this then the world better take a big step back.
I only hope I won't be judged
On a trial that I've won.

The judges sit assembled hid behind some frosted screen,
They cannot see the other side,
Their thoughts do not wander that far from sanity.
And staring through the division at just another victim,
Who struggles at the harsh words put across,
No matter that the trial is unjust.

Then, just as the ice freezes, and blood red snow begins to
fall,
Just before the last time comes,
A new horizon forms a scene.
There is an escape, a tunnel to fresh air
And, though a long one, a path to find the Truth.
This one exception sits there, in between the screen,
Neither here nor there.
But he understands, he can see what they're going through,
He can heal the minds that wander and support the bones
that fall.
And he will carry on, find the strength and patients,
In the end he has the power to set them free

Contemporary Psychiatric Anomalies – Aetiology, Emotion, Mind & Intent

a) aetiolated aetiology

Aetiology is the key to medical acuity – without clarity as to causative factors, medical practice struggles to keep ahead of old wives' tales and populist nostrums. Attributing malaria to 'bad air' was our best guess, before microscopes could show us mosquitoes' entrails. Without electron microscopy, AIDS would devastate in utter medical silence, as Alzheimer's does. Opacity in aetiology strangulates therapeutics.

Contemporary psychiatry argues quite the opposite. Being *"neutral with respect to theories of etiology"* is an *"important methodological innovation"* according to the *Diagnostic and Statistical Manual of Mental Disorders* [1](DSM-IV).   More, DSM-IV declares that *". . a diagnosis does not carry any necessary implications regarding the causes of the individual's mental disorder. . .   Inclusion of a disorder . . does not require that there be knowledge about its etiology"* [2]. Indeed, whereas the first edition of DSM *"reflected Adolf Meyer's . . . view that mental disorders represented reactions of the personality to psychological, social and biological factors,"* which seems eminently practicable, later editions deliberately *"eliminated the term reaction"* [3] [4].

Your recent editorial [5], with the obscurantist correspondence it evoked [6] [7] [8] [9], touches on a psychiatric crisis that is dire in the extreme.   Three points on aetiology.   Firstly, DSM-IV breaches its own claim to aetiological neutrality, by desperately hankering to return psychiatry to the organic medical fold.   Muttering obscurely that 'mind/body dualism' is *"a reductionistic anachronism"*, it tries shamelessly to ditch even the term "Mental Disorders", while obfuscating that *"there is much 'physical' in 'mental' disorders"* [10].   Worse – *"The term 'organic mental disorder' is no longer used in DSM-*

IV because it incorrectly implies that the other mental disorders do not have a biological basis" [11].   Something as obviously non-biological as *"death of a loved one"*, is arbitrarily excluded [12](see below).

Secondly, summarily excommunicating Adolf Meyer without due process betrays Freud's malignant shadow.   Like some sectarian Anti-Christ, Freud has divided psychiatrists for 100 years.   During my 40 years, excess sexuality never once proved pathological.   Freud was a clinical colossus, but his flaws were equally vast.   'Infantile Sexuality' – a conceit he dreamt up to exculpate his own father [13] – is a toxic abomination, poisoning our understanding of child abuse, even today.

Thirdly, medicine's saving virtue is its insistence that empirical clinical data invariably take precedence over any text – "listen to the patient", said Osler "[s]he is telling you the diagnosis".   Empirically, *"death of a loved one"* tops every sensible stress scale, inflicts untold morbidity, while illuminating Attachment Theory.   DSM-IV eliminates it, on the unclinical grounds that it is *"merely an expectable . . response"*.   How sad if such incompetent reasoning lead to clinical incompetence, and from there, however indirectly, to malpractice.

b)   emotionless nosologies

While it may just be possible if lamentable, to proceed as if aetiology were discardable, the same cannot be said for emotions.   It is simply clinically impossible to describe mental diseases without them.   Emotion features larger in mental illhealth, than pain does in physical – a fact no amount of ideological baggage can gainsay.   Indeed the clinical descriptions in DSM-IV are replete with emotions (including *'worries'*) – its preamble and glossaries however, are mute.

DSM-IV perhaps unsurprisingly, declines to grasp the nettle of the fundamental nature of emotions. Emotions after all, are elusive, amorphous, utterly subjective, highly resistant to description, and 100 per cent impervious to objective definition – a taxonomist's nightmare. Yet pain, which is equally subjective and intangible, has been competently dealt with by the medical profession for millennia. The key with pain, is not to argue endlessly about what it 'is' – but to become familiar with it clinically, to learn by clinical practice to distinguish between say dull and colicky pains, and having learnt, to hone one's perception by extensive hands-on experience. Precisely the same applies to emotions. There are subtleties and intricacies which must be observed with emotions – 'denial' and other emotional blind-spots can mislead, as can 'referred pain' – but given training and support, a fruitful clinical understanding can be acquired.

DSM-IV's hazards become obvious if the term 'anxiety' is replaced by 'pain', something it closely resembles in a mental context. 'Generalised Anxiety Disorder' would then be transliterated as 'Generalised Pain Disorder'. Some patients do complain of 'pains all over', but to offer this as a diagnosis invites clinical ridicule. Surely psychiatrists deserve better.

Worse, 'emotionless nosologies' become so unreal that the scope for iatrogenic disease is huge. Who would classify general medical patients into those with mild pain who whimper, and those with severe pain who 'cry out', the former resembling anxiety states, the latter psychoses. Self evidently, most pains are transitory – likewise anxieties and psychoses are episodic. To label a person for life a 'colic', just because she once had this symptom would be a travesty of clinical practice – so why do so with psychosis ?

Even more bizarre would be to divide patients by whether their pain was in the arm, or the leg. Medical staff at Ashworth Maximum Security Hospital follow a similar extraordinary logic by housing their patients in 'Mental Illness' or 'Personality Disorder' wards – a triumph of presumption over acumen.   Once diagnostic categorisation ceases to be harnessed to therapeutics, more sinister purposes emerge – rigid diagnostic unchangeability may comfort doctors, but harm patients.

The mind is the most elastic, fluid and adaptable organ imaginable – humanity's crowning glory, which psychiatric nosologies can either celebrate or suffocate.   For myself, DSM-IV's taxonomy needs inverting – emotions being placed centrally, not peripherally.   Two emotions suffice – fear and anger, with their pathological variants terror and rage.   One or both occur in every case, and bring a consistent therapeutic strategy and a repeatability to my everyday psychiatric practice that DSM-IV would find hard to credit. Personality Disorder it then transpires is 'your mind stopping you doing what you want'.

c)   **pull yourself together**

As if aetiology and emotion were not enough to sink the contemporary psychiatric ship, there are still two further intractables to go – mind and intent.   People in general assume they have a mind, they behave as if they do, and expect others to do the same – in what other organ do mental diseases occur ?   Unhappily the mind is intangible and no objective evidence for its existence can be found, either in the world at large, nor in DSM-IV (as above), nor yet in the *British Journal of Psychiatry*, where it commands one paper in 10 years, apart from Prince Charles [14] who also bewails psychiatry's glaring anomalies.   Intent is unmentionable (as are terror and rage).   Must intangible philosophies always deflect barber surgeons ?   Shouldn't psychiatrists really discuss consciousness more than anaesthetists ?

The mind in reality, is the most complex entity in the entire cosmos, with a higher content of 'unknowability' than anything else we are ever likely to meet.   Though this deters DSM-IV, Freud to his credit embraced both mind and emotion.   What sank Freud was intent.   Like many of our contemporaries, he lived in a Deterministic Clock Work Universe, where Free Will was a mirage, and "pulling yourself together" about as feasible as jumping up and down so as to fly.

Intent is the real joker in today's philosophical pack – how can you define something that then intentionally alters itself ? Small wonder it is taboo throughout Academic Science.   Yet this is an issue larger than one recalcitrant psychiatrist protesting for the curability of paedophilia and psychopathy – it brings psychiatry into conflict first with the law, and then with the fundamentals of democracy.

Legal practice collapses without the concept of intent – when you picked up that spade, did you intend to dig or to kill ? And democracy, especially one based on 'market forces' i.e. consumer choice, is utterly reliant on the electorate making its intentions known.   All convinced democrats believe passionately in human rights and electoral choice and intention – little knowing how mortifying this is for contemporary psychiatry, for psychoanalysis and for too many academics.

Early in my five years at Parkhurst Prison, three murderers expressed their intent to kill me – risk assessment with a personal edge.   Through Emotional Education, and by actively deploying the concepts of Truth Trust and Consent, their intent was re-directed towards more civilised, responsible, adult purposes.   Uniquely in any Maximum Security Prison Wing they later reported that no alarm bells were rung for two years [15].   It is absurd to attempt risk assessment while ignoring intentions.   It helps to find that under every frozen terror exists a personality yearning (and 'intending') to be Sociable, Lovable, and Non-violent [16].